MACHINE DRAWING

MACHINE DRAWING

A TEXT AND PROBLEM BOOK
FOR TECHNICAL STUDENTS
AND DRAFTSMEN

BY

CARL L. SVENSEN, M.E.

ASSISTANT PROFESSOR OF ENGINEERING DRAWING IN THE OHIO STATE UNIVERSITY,
MEMBER AMERICAN SOCIETY OF MECHANICAL ENGINEERS, SOCIETY FOR
THE PROMOTION OF ENGINEERING EDUCATION, ETC.

388 ILLUSTRATIONS

NEW YORK
D. VAN NOSTRAND COMPANY
EIGHT WARREN STREET
1921

PRINTED IN THE UNITED STATES OF AMERICA

PREFACE

Machine drawing may be considered as:

1. A final stage of a course in mechanical drawing.
2. A course in practical drafting.
3. A transition course between mechanical drawing and machine design.
4. An introductory or first course in machine design.
5. A course for the correlation of drawing and engineering.

The importance of such a course is well recognized but the means of attaining success is not so readily available as for many other courses. This book is planned to make available, a guide for the development of an understanding of the relation of machine drawing to engineering. The text is kept as brief as a clear presentation of the subject matter permits. It is designed for advanced courses for students who have had previous instruction in mechanical drawing. A brief chapter on elementary principles is given as an introduction to the course and for review purposes or reference.

A complete treatment of the subject of working drawings, drafting room practice and idiomatic expressions of the engineering language is followed by a chapter on the principles and practice of dimensioning. The classification of size specification by means of two kinds of dimensions, six cases of the elements of dimensioning, and four systems of dimensioning will, it is hoped, make this subject a definite study.

A study of the common machine details, empirical machine design, jigs and fixtures, etc., are included as properly belonging to an advanced course in machine drawing.

A textbook obtains much of its value from the number, variety, and character of the problems which it contains. The collection of problems in this book (about two hundred) is arranged under headings in a single chapter where they can be conveniently found. Necessary instructions, hints, and references to the text are given so that the student has a definite task whether assigned a simple machine part or the study of a complete machine. The problems are presented by layouts or other specifications so that the instructor is relieved of the preliminary details which ordinarily arise when assigning machine drawing studies.

The scope of the text and the variety and extent of the illustrations and problems is such that it is believed that the special needs of thorough courses in machine drawing in technical institutions can be efficiently served.

C. L. S.

COLUMBUS, OHIO,
September, 1921.

7 0 2 6

CONTENTS

Six Cases—Systems of Dimensioning—Location of Dimensions—Methods of Finishing—Dimensioning Arcs and Curves—Dimensioning Angles and Tapers—Dimensioning in Crowded Places—Dimensioning Shafts and Cylindrical Pieces—Dimensioning Wood Constructions—Dimensioning for Interchangeable Manufacture—Limit Dimensions—Basic Dimensions—General Rules—Checking Drawings.

CHAPTER V

Machine Operations—Graphical Data and Dimensions—Engine Details—Pistons—Crossheads—Connecting Rods—Eccentrics—Cranks—Levers, Handles, Etc.—Stuffing Boxes—Fillets, Rounds, Arcs, Etc.—Flanges.

CHAPTER VI

Bearings—Bushings—Bearing Metals—Babbitt—Bearing "Boxes"—Simple Bearings—Hangers—Pulleys—Belt Length—Horsepower Transmitted by Belts—Pulley Proportions—"Crowning"—Rims—Pulley Arms—Split Pulleys.

CHAPTER VII ·

Shafting—Standard Sizes—Special Shafts—To Compute the Diameter of a Shaft—Twisting Moment—Hollow Shaft—Horsepower Transmitted—Table of Constants—Shaft for Bending and Twisting—Shaft Details—A Shafting Drawing—Couplings—Solid Sleeve Couplings—Clamp Couplings—Flange Couplings—Clutch Couplings.

CHAPTER VIII

Jigs and Fixtures—Fixtures—Jigs—Jig and Fixture Drawings—Considerations—A Jig Drawing—A Fixture Drawing—Fixture Design—Standard Parts for Jigs and Fixtures—Standard Bushings—Standard Parts and Details—Shop Appliances—T-Slots, Etc.

CHAPTER IX

Pulleys and Gears—Ratio of Velocities—Gear Teeth—Gear Terms—Spur Gears—Spur Gear Drawing—Bevel Gears—Worm Gearing—Cams—To Draw a Plate Cam—Pitch Line—Roller Modification—Kinds of Motion—Offset Follower—Cam with Flat Follower—Cylindrical Cam.

CHAPTER X

Piping—Uses and Materials—Pipe Sizes—Piping Fittings, Valves, Etc.—Flanged Fittings—Valves—Valve Seats—Conventional Representation—Piping Drawings—Dimensioning—Piping Sketches—Developed or Single Plane Drawings.

CHAPTER XI

MACHINE DRAWING

CHAPTER I

ELEMENTARY PRINCIPLES

1. In the practice of engineering there is a constant dependence upon mechanical drawing as a means of specification for machine constructions. Its use in the industries has led to the development of what might be called applied mechanical drawing as distinguished from the theory taught in mechanical drawing and descriptive geometry. This application has brought about certain practical modifications or variations from theory.

The drawings which represent present practice in the description and specification of machinery are called machine drawings.

2. The Pencil.—For good work it is important that the pencils should be of uniform quality and of the right degree of hardness. Use an H or $2H$ pencil for lettering, figuring, etc., a $4H$ for detail drawings and a $6H$ for design drawings.

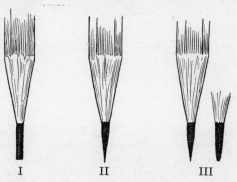

I   II   III

Fig. 1. The Pencil Point.

3. The time consumed as well as the quality of the drawing depend largely upon the attention given to keeping the pencil point carefully sharpened. Remove the wood with a knife as at I, Fig. 1, being particular not to cut the lead. With fine sandpaper or a file shape the lead to a long conical point as at II. For line work many draftsmen use a "chisel" or "wedge" point, shown at III.

4. The Scale.—Scales are used for measuring and "laying-off" distances. For machine drawing the mechanical engineers' (or architects') open divided scale is required. Two common forms are the "flat" scale, Fig. 2, and the "triangular" scale, Fig. 3. The views which repre-

FIG. 2. The Flat Scale.

sent an object are drawn full size when it is practicable to do so. When this is not possible, use proportional or reduced scales to lay off distances on the drawing.

5. The following scales are used on machine drawings, $3'' = 1$ ft., $1\frac{1}{2}'' = 1$ ft., $1'' = 1$ ft., $\frac{3}{4}'' = 1$ ft., $\frac{1}{2}'' = 1$ ft., $\frac{3}{8}'' = 1$ ft., $\frac{1}{4}'' = 1$ ft.,

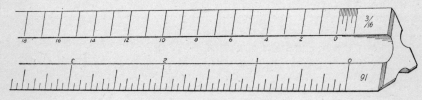

FIG. 3. The Triangular Scale.

$\frac{3}{16}'' = 1$ ft., and $\frac{1}{8}'' = 1$ ft. The scale of $3'' = 1$ ft., is often called quarter size, and $1\frac{1}{2}'' = 1$ ft., is called eighth size. These two reductions are much used on detail drawings.

6. The scale $3'' = 1$ ft., means that the measurements on the drawing are one fourth the measurements of the actual object, or that each one fourth inch on the drawing represents one inch on the object. In this case a distance equal to three inches is divided into 12 parts, each part representing one inch. These parts are further divided to represent quarter inches and other fractions.

7. Half size ($6'' = 1$ ft.) drawings are worked from the full size scale. In such cases use the half inch for an inch. *Never divide* the dimensions of the piece when drawing to a reduced scale. Measure with the reduced scale and *think* full size. *Always* put figures representing the full size of the machine or part on the drawing regardless of the scale. Distances measured with different scales are illustrated in Fig. 4.

8. Inking.—The ruling or drawing pen is used for inking the lines after the pencil drawing is finished. Black drawing ink is always used for making drawings. Ink is placed between the nibs of the pen with the quill which is attached to the ink bottle stopper. Care must be taken

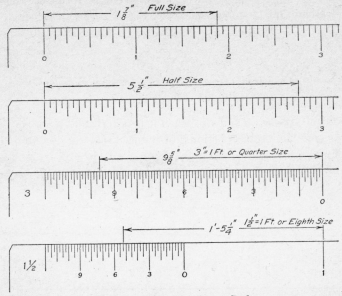

FIG. 4. Measurements to Scale.

to prevent ink from getting on the outside of the pen. The proper amount of ink is shown in Fig. 5.

Full Size

FIG. 5.

When inking, the pen should be held in a nearly vertical position and guided by the T square or triangle. Keep the point of the pen away from the angle formed by the paper and the guide. Do not hold the pen too tightly, or press against the guide. Both nibs of the pen must touch the paper. Frequent cleaning of the pen is necessary to obtain good, sharp lines.

9. The pens for the compasses are filled and cared for in the same way. The legs of the compasses should be perpendicular to the paper and adjusted so that both nibs of the pen touch the paper. When drawing small or short arcs a smaller amount of ink should be used in the bow pen to avoid wider "spots" at the ends of the arcs. When setting to a

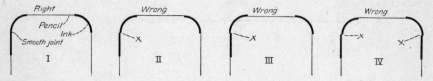

FIG. 6.   Joining Lines and Arcs.

radius, the ink line should come exactly over the pencil line to make sure of good joints at points of tangency as in Fig. 6, which also shows the effect of inking on the inside or outside of a pencil line.

10. Dotted lines should be drawn with careful attention to detail. A dotted line starts with a dot when it represents the extent of a surface as at *A*, Fig. 7, but when part of a line is full a space is left between the full line and the first dot as at *B*. At a corner the two dots which form the angle should touch. Dotted arcs always start at tangent points as in Fig. 8 which shows a "one dot," a "two dot" and a "three dot" arc.

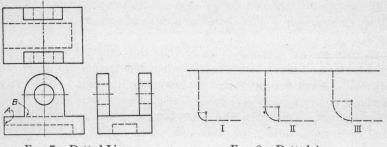

FIG. 7.   Dotted Lines.   FIG. 8.   Dotted Arcs.

Note the positions of the centers and tangent points. The dots must be of uniform length and spacing whether used for arcs or straight lines. Make dotted lines much lighter than full lines to give contrast to the drawing.

The order of penciling and inking when making a working drawing is given in Arts. 75 and 76. The general order of inking is: arcs and circles; horizontal lines; vertical lines; inclined lines.

11. Character of Lines.—All pencil lines should be fine, clear, and sharp. For most purposes continuous pencil lines may be used. If the drawing is not to be inked the final lines must be distinct but not too wide. Pencil lines for dimensions, sections, etc., should be fine, gray lines. A 2*H* pencil is suitable for making dotted lines on pencil drawings.

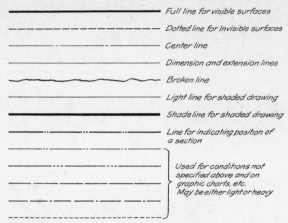

FIG. 9. Sample Lines.

If the drawing is to be inked, it is not necessary to use different kinds of lines for penciling. The character and weight of ink lines is given in Fig. 9.

12. For general drawings a fairly wide line should be adopted as it wears better and gives better results when blue prints are made. The width of line will depend somewhat upon the drawing. Large, simple drawings require a wide line, while small intricate drawings necessitate narrower lines. Drawings which are large and still have considerable detail in parts require more than one width of line. An experienced draftsman will use wide lines for the large and simple parts, reducing them for the complicated places in such manner that the different widths of lines are not noticeable.

13. Cleaning and Erasing.—Drawings which have been worked over for a length of time become soiled, due to rubbing over the pencil lines with the T square and triangles, perspiration from the hands, and the dust which settles on them. For this reason, the drawing board, tools and instruments should be wiped with a piece of cloth before starting work. Do not sharpen a pencil over the drawing or board. Keep the hands clean, especially if they have a tendency to become moist. All the tools should be cleaned occasionally with a damp cloth and thoroughly dried before using. Sometimes the part of the drawing not being worked on can be covered with an extra sheet of paper.

14. Either pencil or ink lines can be erased when necessary by using a soft red or green rubber. Always rub in the direction of the line. Do not use a knife or ink eraser as they destroy the surface of the paper or tracing cloth. Be sure that an ink line is dry before erasing it. Care and patience are necessary when erasing ink. Do not dig into the paper or overheat the eraser by attempting to remove a line too quickly. An erasing shield of celluloid or metal is convenient to save lines which are not to be removed. Art gum is very useful for erasing pencil lines and for cleaning the entire drawing when it is finished.

15. Accuracy and Neatness.—The question of time or efficiency enters into all work and should be considered in studying engineering subjects. Accuracy and neatness not only save time in the study of drafting but are absolute essentials if worth while progress is to be made.

Be sure that the paper is tacked down *flat* on the board and that the T square head is not loose.

Keep all instruments clean and in proper adjustment, ready for use. Always clean lettering and ruling pens before filling and after using.

Keep the pencil points sharp *all the time.* Draw lightly—do not groove the paper.

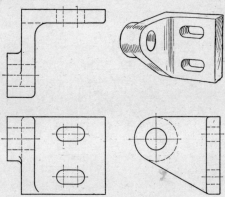

Fig. 10. A Three-View Drawing.

Pencil lines may run a short distance beyond corners when first laying out but do not draw them clear across the sheet. Do not draw extra lines as it takes time to erase them. Consider the order in which the lines of the different views are drawn, working from the general center and "block in" lines to the details. Make similar measurements at one time. Have a system and follow it.

Do not slight small details or have "fuzzy," indistinct corners and joints. Make every part of the drawing accurately to scale and perfectly clear. Too much freehand work, dull pencils, lack of contrast in lines, inaccurate measurements and lack of exactness in representation, make "sloppy" drawings which often prove very expensive. Clear thinking should be expressed in clear, easily read drawings.

16. Shop Drawings.—Drawings for machinery are made up of views obtained by orthographic projection and arranged in accord with the third angle. The number of views depends upon the object or construction to be described, two or three generally being sufficient. Each view shows the object as seen from a different position; from above (top view), from in front (front view), and from one side (side view), Fig. 10.

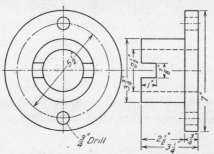

FIG. 11. A Two-View Drawing.

17. A two view drawing is shown in Fig. 11. Three views of a blacksmith's "sow" are given in Fig. 12. The top view shows surfaces A', B and A. The meaning of the horizontal lines which limit surface B cannot be understood without looking at the end view which shows that the surface B is on a lower level than surfaces A and A'.

The representation of a sloping surface is shown in the drawing of the

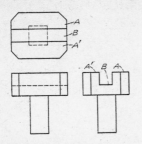

FIG. 12. Reading a Drawing.

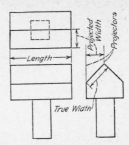

FIG. 13. "Projected" Area.

"swage," Fig. 13. The "projected area" of such a surface is less than its true area.

The representation of a cylindrical surface is illustrated in Fig. 14 by the shaded areas. If a cylinder has its axis perpendicular to a plane

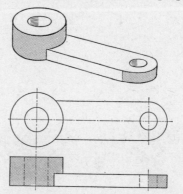

FIG. 14. Projection of Curved Surfaces.

its projection on that plane is a circle. When the axis is parallel to a plane the cylinder appears as a rectangle.

18. Placing Views.—The views are generally arranged as illustrated in Figs. 10 and 15. This is called the *first position for the right side view.*

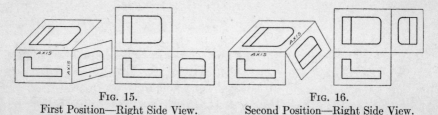

FIG. 15.   FIG. 16.
First Position—Right Side View.   Second Position—Right Side View.

Sometimes, however, it is desirable to revolve the side plane about an axis formed by its intersection with the horizontal plane. This gives the *second position of the right side view,* Fig. 16. The second position is

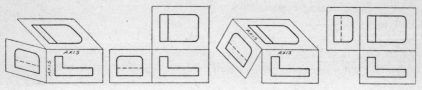

FIG. 17.   FIG. 18.
First Position—Left Side View.   Second Position—Left Side View.

used when a piece is rather flat and wide. It allows the use of a larger scale. Sometimes it is the only way in which the views can be contained on a given size of drawing paper.

The *first position of the left side view* is shown in Fig. 17, and the *second position* in Fig. 18.

19. Auxiliary Views.—When it is desirable to show the true size or shape of a surface which is not parallel to the usual planes of projection,

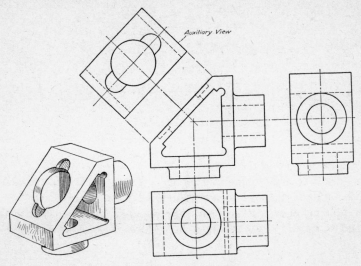

FIG. 19. Auxiliary View.

an *auxiliary view* is drawn, Fig. 19. The chart Fig. 20, illustrates two methods of solution as applied to three cases.

20. Sectional Views.—When it is necessary to show the interior of an object or machine more clearly than can be done with dotted lines, an imaginary cutting plane is used. The part of the object in front of the cutting plane is removed, leaving the object as in Fig. 21. The cut surface is section lined and the view is called a section. The subject of sections is treated at length in Chapter III.

21. Engineering Handbooks.—The value of handbooks for designers and engineers is too well established to require comment. There is a mass of detail information and dimensions more or less standardized, which must be adhered to when making machine drawings. Every engineer should possess at least one handbook which bears directly upon his work and should learn how to use it. Use a handbook when checking

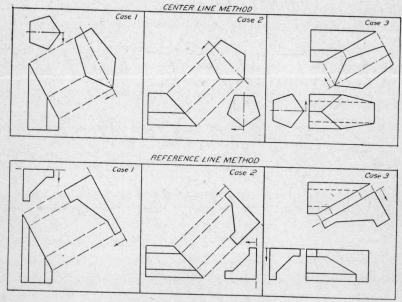

FIG. 20. Auxiliary View Chart.

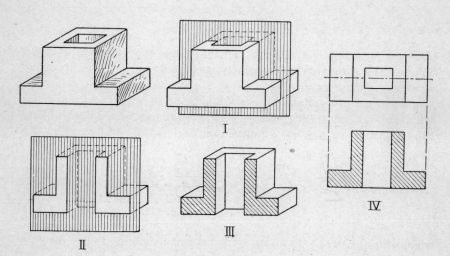

FIG. 21. Sectional View.

drawings of machinery as well as when making new drawings. Learn the location of such tables as are most frequently used.

FIG. 22. Capital Letters and Numbers.

22. A.S.M.E. and Other Standards.—Reliable information can be obtained from the publications of the various engineering societies. Some of the standards are so widely used that the machine draftsman must be familiar with them. The American Society of Mechanical Engineers publishes standards for: Boilers (Paper 1469), Graphic Presentation (Paper 101X), Machine Screws (Papers 1142 and 1142A), Pipe Flanges, Fittings, etc. (Papers 1430 and 1654), and for many other

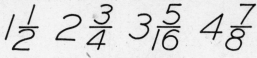

FIG. 23. Slant Fractions.

engineering matters. For automobile work the standard data sheets of the Society of Automotive Engineers should be consulted. The standards of some of the large manufacturers are in universal use.

23. Lettering.—A certain degree of expertness in lettering is assumed to be one of the qualifications of present-day engineers. The necessary requirements are included in Chap. II of the "Essentials of Drafting."

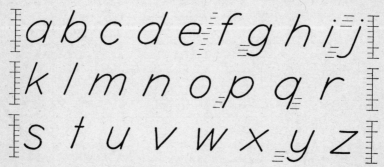

FIG. 24. Lower Case Letters.

The proportions and forms of plain slant letters and numbers are shown in Figs. 22, 23, and 24. The slope is about three to eight. Note the arrows which indicate the directions in which the various lines are drawn. A scale of units is given at the ends of the lines. By placing a straight edge across the page and coincident with the same scale line at both ends, the positions of the horizontal strokes of the letters can be observed. The figures under each letter indicate the width in terms of the same units as are given for the height.

FIG. 25. A Hand Lettered Title.

24. The proportions of the fractions in comparison with whole numbers are shown in Fig. 23. The division line is always horizontal with a small space between the fraction numbers and the line.

25. Titles for drawings vary a great deal as an inspection of a few blue prints will show. The titles for detail drawings may or may not contain the name and location of the company. The name of the machine, its size and number, the names of details, the scale, the date, and the names or initials of the draftsman and engineer should be given. A hand lettered title is shown in Fig. 25 and a printed title form in Fig. 26. The record strip is much used and consists of a narrow strip ex-

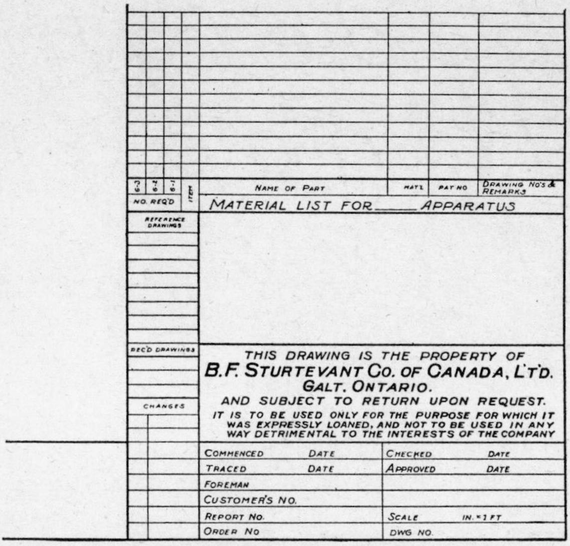

FIG. 23. A Printed Title.

tending the whole length or width of the sheet. It contains the title, record of changes, general notes and other desired information.

CHAPTER II

FASTENINGS FOR MACHINERY

26. Kinds of Fastenings.—Practical requirements of manufacture and use necessitate the use of separate pieces in the construction of machinery. The common fastenings are screws, bolts, rivets, pins, keys, hooks, slides, etc.

27. Screw Threads.—In addition to their use as fastenings, screws are used to transmit motion, to apply force, and for the adjustment of parts. A screw is a cylinder with a helical groove which forms the thread, Fig. 27.

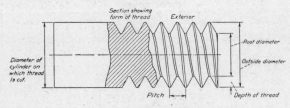

Fig. 27. Screw Thread.

The usual forms of screw threads are given in Fig. 28. The form shown at I is the United States Standard, also called Sellers, or Franklin Institute. The V's are flattened which makes the thread stronger than if left sharp as in the V thread shown at II. The Whitworth, or English Standard thread is shown at III. These three forms are well adapted for fastening parts of machinery together.

28. The square thread, shown at IV, and the Acme thread, shown at V, are used for transmitting forces and motions. The Acme thread permits the use of a split nut. The buttress or breechlock thread is shown at VI. It is designed to take pressure in one direction only. This form has the strength in shear of the V form but avoids the tendency to burst the nut. A similar form called the Harvey grip, is shown at VII. The knuckle or rounded thread is illustrated at VIII. This thread is often rolled in sheet metal, as for screw caps, electric fixtures, etc. For some purposes it is cast in a mold.

29. Pitch and Lead.—The pitch of a screw thread is the distance from one thread point to the next, measured parallel to the axis. The lead is the distance which the screw will move along the axis for one turn. For a single thread the pitch and lead are equal. For a double thread the lead is two times the pitch.

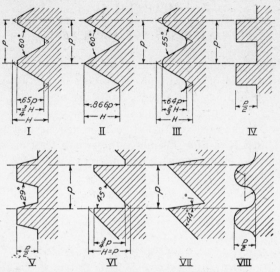

FIG. 28. Forms of Screw Threads.

30. Conventional Representation of Screw Threads.—It is not often necessary to draw the helix representing a screw thread, as there are a number of conventional representations in use designed to save time. These serve the purpose just as well as the true representation would do. Common methods are shown in Fig. 29. The representation given at V is preferred for ordinary drawings. It is not necessary to draw the pitch

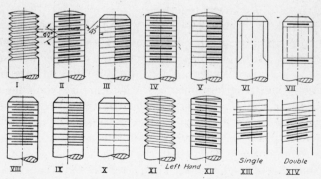

FIG. 29. Conventional Drawings of Screw Threads.

to scale.   The distance between lines is estimated and arranged to avoid
crowding so as to give a pleasing appearance.   The lines may be at an
angle with, or perpendicular to the axis of the screw.   The angle when
used is determined by one half the pitch for single threads, XIII, or the
whole pitch for double threads, XIV.   For such representations as II
and IV light pencil guide lines should be drawn parallel to the axis of
the screw to limit the heavy lines which represent the root diameter of
the screw.   The 60° lines show how the distance between the guide lines
is determined.   The tops of the threads are represented by fine lines.

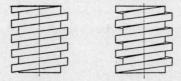

FIG. 30.   Square Threads.

Two distinctive representations for square threads are shown in
Fig. 30.

31. Threaded Holes.—Representations for threaded holes are shown
in plan, elevation, and section in Fig. 31.   It will be observed that the

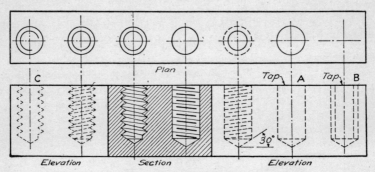

FIG. 31.   Threaded Holes.

lines representing the threads slope in the opposite direction when the
hole is shown in section.   The reason for this is that the far side of the
thread is seen.   Either single or double circles may be used in the plan,
and any of the plans may be used with any of the sections or elevations.
The lines representing the roots of the threads when visible are made
heavy if inked, but when dotted all lines should be the same either in
ink or pencil.   When the representations shown at A and B are used,

they should always be marked "Tap." For small diameters the V's may be drawn in freehand and the thread lines omitted as at *C*. When

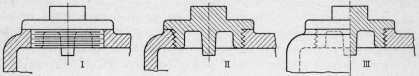

FIG. 32.   Screw Threads in Section.

two or more threaded pieces are shown together, the methods of Fig. 32 are used.   Clearness may be preserved when drawing threaded pieces in elevation or section by using the methods of Fig. 33 at II, III, and IV where the thread lines are left out.

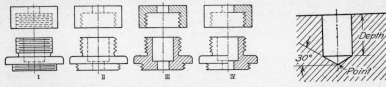

FIG. 33. Thread Representations.   FIG. 34.

Where a hole does not go all the way through a piece, the angle of the end of the drill leaves the end of the hole pointed, drawn with 30° lines as shown in Fig. 34.

TABLE 1

DIMENSIONS OF U. S. STANDARD THREADS

Diameter	Threads per Inch	Diameter of Tap Drill	Root Diameter	Root Area
$1/4$	20	$3/16$	.185	.026
$5/16$	18	$1/4$	.241	.045
$3/8$	16	$5/16$	.294	.068
$7/16$	14	$23/64$	.345	.093
$1/2$	13	$13/32$	.400	.126
$9/16$	12	$15/32$	.454	.162
$5/8$	11	$17/32$	.507	.202
$3/4$	10	$5/8$	.620	.302
$7/8$	9	$3/4$	.731	.420
1	8	$27/32$	.838	.551
$1 1/8$	7	$31/32$	.940	.693
$1 1/4$	7	$1 3/32$	1.065	.889
$1 3/8$	6	$1 3/16$	1.159	1.054
$1 1/2$	6	$1 5/16$	1.284	1.293
$1 5/8$	$5 1/2$	$1 13/32$	1.389	1.515
$1 3/4$	5	$1 1/2$	1.491	1.744
$1 7/8$	5	$1 5/8$	1.616	2.049
2	$4 1/2$	$1 3/4$	1.711	2.300

32. Specifications of Screw Threads.—For U. S. Standard bolts the number of threads per inch is fixed as given in Table 1, which gives other useful information.

Notes and abbreviations used on drawings to specify screw threads are as follows: The initials R.H. or L.H. are used to denote right hand or left hand.

"*8 Thds. U.S.S.*" means eight threads per inch, United States Standard thread.

"*14 Thds. U.S.F.*" means fourteen threads per inch United States form.

"*32 Thds. A.S.M.E.Std.*" means 32 threads per inch, American Society Mechanical Engineers Standard Machine screw thread.

"*B.S.W.*" means British Standard, Whitworth or English thread.

"*B.S.F.*" means British Standard fine screw thread.

Other notes and information may be understood by consulting the handbooks published by "American Machinist" and "Machinery."

33. Pipe Threads.—Wrought pipe is specified by its nominal inside diameter for sizes up to 12″. Actual diameters are given in Table 27 which also gives the number of threads per inch. Tables 28 and 29 give dimensions of extra strong and double extra strong pipe.

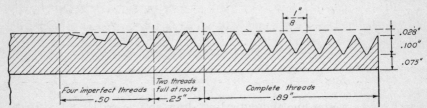

FIG. 35.   Enlarged Section of 2½″ Pipe Thread.

Pipe threads have an angle of 60°, and have the top and bottom of the V rounded. The threads are cut on a taper of three fourths inch per foot. The form is shown in Fig. 35.

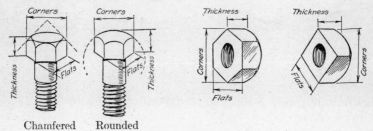

Chamfered   Rounded
FIG. 36.   U. S. Standard Bolts.

34. U. S. Standard Bolts and Nuts.—Ordinary hexagonal and square bolt heads and nuts are made with U. S. Standard proportions. The chamfered and rounded types are shown in Fig. 36. The dimensions are based upon the diameter of the bolt. The distance across flats of either hex or square is made equal to $1\frac{1}{2}$ D + $\frac{1}{8}''$. The thickness of a head is one half the distance across flats or $\frac{3}{4}$ D + $\frac{1}{16}''$. The thickness of a nut is equal to the diameter of the bolt.

35. To Draw a Bolt Head or Nut Across Flats.—To draw a hex bolt head or nut, Figs. 37 and 38, draw the center line, diameter of bolt, and

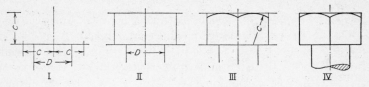

FIG. 37.   Hex Bolt Head Across Flats.

line locating under side of head as at I. For a bolt head lay off the distance C, equal to one half the distance across flats, in the three places shown at I and draw lines as at II. With C as a radius and center half

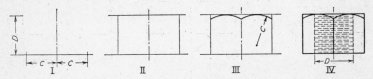

FIG. 38.   Hex Nut Across Flats.

way between center line and outer line, draw arcs as at III and complete as shown at IV. For a nut the dimensions are the same *except* the thickness which is equal to the diameter of the bolt, Fig. 38.

36. To draw a square bolt head across flats, Fig. 39, proceed as for

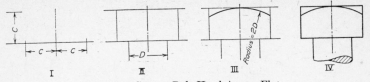

FIG. 39.   Square Bolt Head Across Flats.

the hex form but draw a single arc with center on center line and radius equal to twice the diameter of bolt. A square nut is drawn in the same way *except* that the thickness is equal to the diameter of the bolt.

37. To Draw a Bolt Head or Nut Across Corners.—For a bolt head draw center line, diameter of bolt, and line locating under side of head. Construct diagram shown in Fig. 40 at I, thus obtaining distances B,

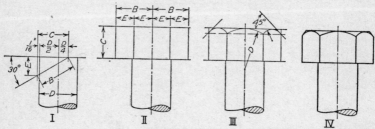

FIG. 40. Hex Bolt Head Across Corners.

C and E. With dividers take distances from the diagram to locate lines on the drawing as shown at II. Draw center arc with radius equal to diameter of bolt. Draw side arcs with radius found by trial so that they have the same rise as center arc as indicated at III. Draw 45° chamfer lines and complete as at IV.

For a nut the dimensions are the same *except* the thickness.

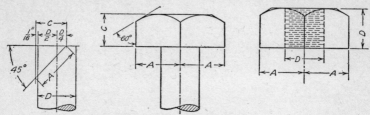

FIG. 41. Square Bolt Head and Nut.

38. To draw a square bolt head or nut across corners refer to Fig. 41.

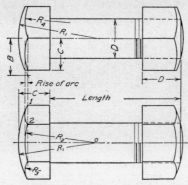

FIG. 42. Rounded Type.

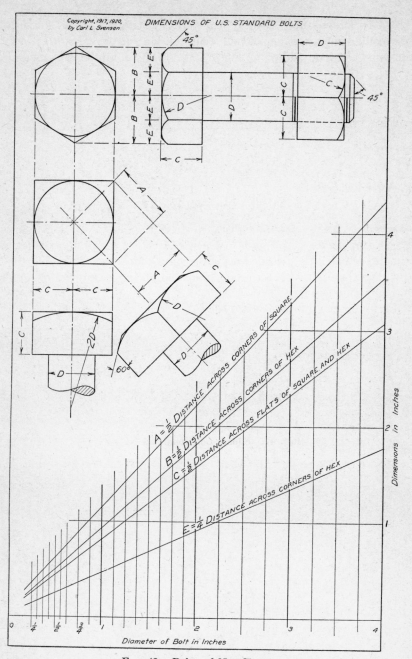

Fig. 43. Bolt and Nut Chart.

The distance across flats and thickness of bolt head is the same as for the hex form. Note the radii of the arcs, the 30° chamfer angle, and the 45° angle in the diagram.

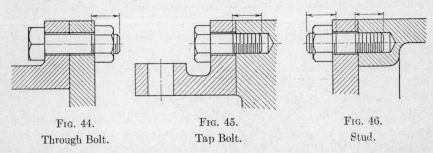

FIG. 44.   FIG. 45.   FIG. 46.

Through Bolt.   Tap Bolt.   Stud.

39. A rounded type of bolt head and nut are shown in Fig. 42. The same proportions hold as for the chamfered type. The radius R_1 is two times the diameter of the bolt. The dotted line through point 1 locates point 2. The radius R_2 has its center at O and is equal to the distance $O - 2$. Radii R_3 and R_4 must have the same rise as radius R_2. They are found by trial to fit the rise.

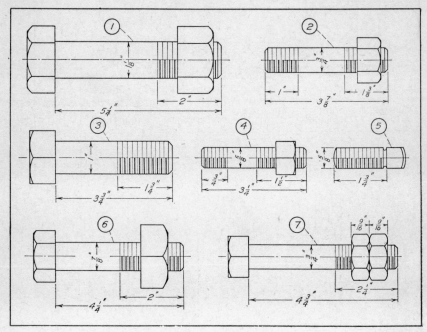

FIG. 47.   Bolt Drawing.

40. Bolt Chart.—The chart, Fig. 43, is for use when drawing full size bolts and nuts. The distances can be transferred with the dividers or compasses. Horizontal distances give the diameters of the bolts. Distances vertically from the base line to where a vertical line through a given diameter crosses the inclined lines, gives the necessary distances. The inclined lines are lettered to correspond with the distances shown on the drawings.

41. Bolts and Studs.—Three common forms of bolts are the through bolt, Fig. 44, the tap bolt, Fig. 45, and the stud or stud bolt Fig. 46. When possible the through bolt should be used as it requires only drilled holes. The tap bolt is used as a permanent fastening in cases where a cap screw (Art. 44) is not desired. When there are parts which must be removed often or where the threads might rust in, studs are used if through bolts are not practicable. The length of thread must be designated in all cases and is indicated in the figures.

TABLE 2

DIMENSIONS OF U. S. STANDARD BOLT HEADS AND NUTS

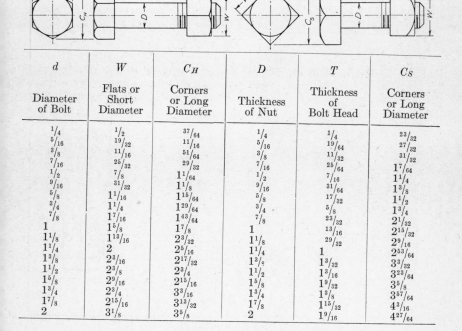

d	W	C_H	D	T	C_S
Diameter of Bolt	Flats or Short Diameter	Corners or Long Diameter	Thickness of Nut	Thickness of Bolt Head	Corners or Long Diameter
$1/4$	$1/2$	$37/64$	$1/4$	$1/4$	$23/32$
$5/16$	$19/32$	$11/16$	$5/16$	$19/64$	$27/32$
$3/8$	$11/16$	$51/64$	$3/8$	$11/32$	$31/32$
$7/16$	$25/32$	$29/32$	$7/16$	$25/64$	$1^7/64$
$1/2$	$7/8$	$1^1/64$	$1/2$	$7/16$	$1^1/4$
$9/16$	$31/32$	$1^1/8$	$9/16$	$31/64$	$1^3/8$
$5/8$	$1^1/16$	$1^{15}/64$	$5/8$	$17/32$	$1^1/2$
$3/4$	$1^1/4$	$1^{29}/64$	$3/4$	$5/8$	$1^3/4$
$7/8$	$1^7/16$	$1^{43}/64$	$7/8$	$23/32$	$2^1/8$
1	$1^5/8$	$1^7/8$	1	$13/16$	$2^{15}/32$
$1^1/8$	$1^{13}/16$	$2^3/32$	$1^1/8$	$29/32$	$2^9/16$
$1^1/4$	2	$2^5/16$	$1^1/4$	1	$2^{53}/64$
$1^3/8$	$2^3/16$	$2^{17}/32$	$1^3/8$	$1^3/32$	$3^3/32$
$1^1/2$	$2^3/8$	$2^3/4$	$1^1/2$	$1^3/16$	$3^{23}/64$
$1^5/8$	$2^9/16$	$2^{15}/16$	$1^5/8$	$1^9/32$	$3^5/8$
$1^3/4$	$2^3/4$	$3^3/16$	$1^3/4$	$1^3/8$	$3^{57}/64$
$1^7/8$	$2^{15}/16$	$3^{13}/32$	$1^7/8$	$1^{15}/32$	$4^3/16$
2	$3^1/8$	$3^5/8$	2	$1^9/16$	$4^{27}/64$

42. A stud may be made tight in a hole by having the threads jam near the bottom or the top of the hole. For the second condition clearance must be allowed.

43. Since bolt heads and nuts are standard, only three dimensions are necessary on a drawing. For a bolt these are diameter, length from under side of head, and length of thread measured from end of bolt. For a stud, give the diameter, total length, and length of thread measured from each end. A bolt drawing is shown in Fig. 47.

Dimensions of U. S. Standard bolts are given in Table 2.

44. Cap Screws.—Hexagonal and square head cap screws are similar in appearance to rounded type bolts but the distance across flats is less than standard and the thickness of head is more than standard. Various

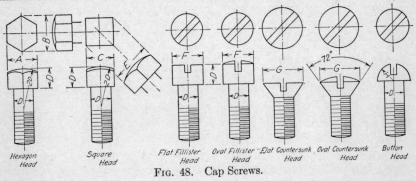

Hexagon Head   Square Head   Flat Fillister Head   Oval Fillister Head   Flat Countersunk Head   Oval Countersunk Head   Button Head

Fig. 48. Cap Screws.

forms of heads are shown in Fig. 48 and dimensions for drawing them are given in Table 3. Cap screws are designated by their diameter in inches which are given as fractions starting at $1/4''$, and by length in inches.

		Old Number	New Size
Flat Head	**Flat Fillister Head**	0	.060
82°	D	1	.073
B = 2A-.008	B=1.64A-.009	2	.086
C = A-.008 / 1.739	C=.66A-.002	3	.099
D = .173A+.015	D=.173A+.015	4	.112
E = $\frac{C}{2}$	E= $\frac{C}{2}$	5	.125
		6	.138
		7	.151
		8	.164
		9	.177
Round Head	**Oval Fillister Head**	10	.190
		12	.216
		14	.242
B = 1.85A-.005	B=1.64A-.009	16	.268
C = .7A	C=.66A-.002	18	.294
D = .173A+.015	D=.173A+.015		
E = $\frac{C}{2}$+.01	E=$\frac{F}{2}$	20	.320
	F=.134B+C	22	.346
		24	.372
		26	.398
		28	.424
		30	.450

Fig. 49. Machine Screws.

TABLE 3
DIMENSIONS OF CAP SCREWS

Diameter	Flats of Hex	Flats of Square	Thickness of Heads—Hex Square—Fillister	Diameter of Button Head	Diameter of Countersunk Head
$1/8$	....	....	....	$7/32$	$1/4$
$3/16$	....	....	....	$5/16$	$3/8$
$1/4$	$7/16$	$3/8$	$1/4$	$7/16$	$15/32$
$5/16$	$1/2$	$7/16$	$5/16$	$9/16$	$5/8$
$3/8$	$9/16$	$1/2$	$3/8$	$5/8$	$3/4$
$7/16$	$5/8$	$9/16$	$7/16$	$3/4$	$13/16$
$1/2$	$3/4$	$5/8$	$1/2$	$13/16$	$7/8$
$9/16$	$13/16$	$11/16$	$9/16$	$15/16$	1
$5/8$	$7/8$	$3/4$	$5/8$	1	$1\,1/8$
$3/4$	1	$7/8$	$3/4$	$1\,1/4$	$1\,3/8$
$7/8$	$1\,1/8$	$1\,1/8$	$7/8$	....	....
1	$1\,1/4$	$1\,1/4$	1	....	....

45. Machine Screws.—These are small screws especially adapted for use with small parts of machines. The heads are made in different forms as named in Fig. 49. The sizes of machine screws are often designated by numbers. The diameters are in decimals of an inch from .060″ to .450″. Finer pitch threads are used than for U. S. Std. bolts.

46. Set Screws.—These are screws with a small head or none at all, and with variously formed ends, used for holding pulleys in position on shafts and preventing relative motion of parts under similar conditions.

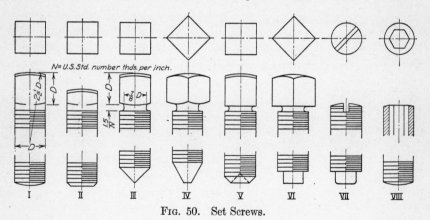

N= U.S. Std. number thds. per inch.

FIG. 50. Set Screws.

Several forms are illustrated in Fig. 50. Any combination of point and head can be used. Some proportions are given in the figures. A projecting set screw on a revolving pulley is a source of great danger, and should be avoided. The many forms of headless and hollow set screws obtainable make the use of other forms unnecessary in such cases.

47. S.A.E. Bolts.—The forms and dimensions of the Society of Automotive Engineers standard bolts are given in Fig. 51 and Table 4. These

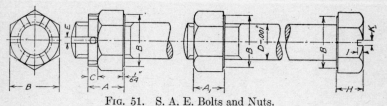

Fig. 51. S. A. E. Bolts and Nuts.

bolts have finer pitch threads and shorter distance across flats than U. S. Std. The nuts are castellated for convenience in locking by use of a cotter pin.

48. Miscellaneous Bolts.—Several forms of bolts are illustrated and named in Fig. 52. They are used under special conditions. The names

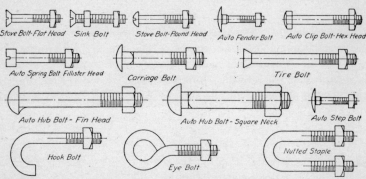

Fig. 52. Miscellaneous Bolts.

have been derived from the use or form of the bolts.

49. Miscellaneous Screws.—A number of screws are shown in Fig. 53. The common wood screw is made in a large variety of sizes and with different forms of heads. Lag screws are used for somewhat heavy wood

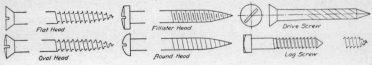

Fig. 53. Miscellaneous Screws.

constructions and for fastening machines or parts of machines to wood. The figure shows the methods of representation for the various screws.

TABLE 4

DIMENSIONS OF S.A.E. BOLTS

D	Thds. per Inch	A	A_1	B	C	E	H	I	K
$1/4$	28	$9/32$	$7/32$	$7/16$	$3/32$	$5/64$	$3/16$	$3/32$.	$1/16$
$5/16$	24	$21/64$	$17/64$	$1/2$	$3/32$	$5/64$	$15/64$	$7/64$	$1/16$
$3/8$	24	$13/32$	$21/64$	$9/16$	$1/8$	$1/8$	$9/32$	$1/8$	$3/32$
$7/16$	20	$29/64$	$3/8$	$5/8$	$1/8$	$1/8$	$21/64$	$1/8$	$3/32$
$1/2$	20	$9/16$	$7/16$	$3/4$	$3/16$	$1/8$	$3/8$	$1/8$	$3/32$
$9/16$	18	$39/64$	$31/64$	$7/8$	$3/16$	$5/32$	$27/64$	$1/8$	$3/32$
$5/8$	18	$23/32$	$35/64$	$15/16$	$1/4$	$5/32$	$15/32$	$1/8$	$3/32$
$11/16$	16	$49/64$	$19/32$	1	$1/4$	$5/32$	$33/64$	$1/8$	$3/32$
$3/4$	16	$13/16$	$21/32$	$1 1/16$	$1/4$	$5/32$	$9/16$	$1/8$	$3/32$
$7/8$	14	$29/32$	$49/64$	$1 1/4$	$1/4$	$5/32$	$21/32$	$1/8$	$3/32$
1	14	1	$7/8$	$1 7/16$	$1/4$	$5/32$	$3/4$	$1/8$	$3/32$
$1 1/8$	12	$1 5/32$	$63/64$	$1 5/8$	$5/16$	$7/32$	$27/32$	$7/32$	$5/32$
$1 1/4$	12	$1 1/4$	$1 3/32$	$1 13/16$	$5/16$	$7/32$	$15/16$	$7/32$	$5/32$
$1 3/8$	12	$1 13/32$	$1 13/64$	2	$3/8$	$1/4$	$1 1/32$	$1/4$	$3/16$
$1 1/2$	12	$1 1/2$	$1 5/16$	$2 3/16$	$3/8$	$1/4$	$1 1/8$	$1/4$	$3/16$

Screws are specified by their diameter, length and form. The diameter is generally given by gauge number. The length for flat head screws, stove bolts, etc., includes the head. For oval head screws the counter sink is included in the length. For round head wood screws about one half the head is included in the length. For lag screws the length is measured from under head to point.

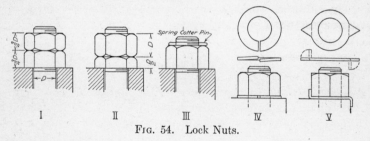

FIG. 54. Lock Nuts.

50. Locking Devices.—The vibration of machinery often causes nuts to become loose if they are not provided with some form of locking device. The commonest method is to use two nuts. They may be full size, three fourth's thickness, or one full and one half thickness. The castle nut illustrated in Fig. 51 is a good method. Lock washers of various kinds are effective. Other arrangements are shown in Fig. 54.

51. Flanges and Bolting.—A method of finding the diameter of bolt circle and diameter of flange is illustrated in Fig. 55. For through bolts the explanation applies to conditions shown at I and II. Draw the desired fillet at r_1. This may be taken at about $t/4$. Lay off X, equal to

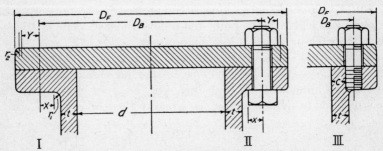

Fig. 55.   Circle of Drilling and Flange Diameter.

one half distance across flats of bolt head, and Y equal to one half distance across corners of nut. The diameter of the bolt circle, D_B, may now be found by laying a scale on the drawing and selecting a dimension. This will be equal to or greater than, $d + 2 (t + r_1 + X)$, and may be taken at the nearest larger $1/8$th inch. The flange diameter may then be obtained by laying out the distance Y, as indicated, and using the scale to find a dimension equal to, or greater than $D_B + 2 (Y + r_2)$. The radius r_2 may be taken at $1/8$th to $1/16$th the thickness of the flange.

When studs are used, the diameters D_B and D_F may be very much decreased as at III. The distance C should be about equal to t, although if necessary it can be made equal to one half the diameter of the bolt.

52. Strength and Number of Bolts.—The strength of a bolt in tension is the strength of the root area. The tensile strength of U. S. Standard threads is given in Table 5. When the load is applied as at I, Fig. 56 the stress is found by the formula $S = P/A$. This is direct tension with no initial stress. At II the bolt is used for holding a cover plate or

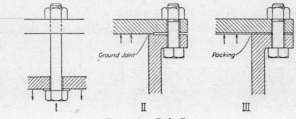

Fig. 56.   Bolt Stress.

cylinder where a ground joint is used. If the bolt lengthens under pressure the joint will open. The nuts must be screwed up so that the stress in the bolt will be equal to or greater than the stress due to pressure against the plate. At III an elastic packing material is used. When the nut is tightened the packing is compressed. The pressure against the plate will lengthen the bolts and relieve them of some of the stress due to the packing which is less compressed.

53. The total stress in the bolts may be that due to tightening plus that due to pressure. This may be further increased by the twisting stress by an amount equal to 10 per cent. or more of the load stress. The stress due to tightening may be equal to the load stress.

TABLE 5

TENSILE STRENGTH OF U. S. STANDARD SCREW THREADS

Diameter	Threads per Inch	Total Strength of One Bolt for Unit Stresses of		
		4000	5000	6000
$1/4$	20	105	135	160
$3/8$	16	270	340	405
$1/2$	13	500	625	750
$5/8$	11	805	1010	1210
$3/4$	10	1200	1500	1800
$7/8$	9	1680	2100	2520
$17/8$	8	2200	2750	3300
$11/8$	7	2770	3460	4160
$11/4$	7	3120	3900	4680
$13/8$	6	4240	5300	6360
$11/2$	6	5120	6400	7680
$15/8$	$51/2$	6120	7650	9180
$13/4$	5	7040	8800	10560
$17/8$	5	8120	10150	12180
2	$41/2$	9200	11500	13800

54. To figure the load on bolts for cover plates or cylinder heads divide the total pressure by the number of bolts. The size is often found by using a low value for the working stress.

55. To figure the number of bolts, divide the total pressure by the working strength of the size of bolt selected. To maintain a tight joint under pressure requires careful judgment in selecting size of bolt, location of drilling and distance between bolts. The distance X between bolts should not generally exceed 4 to 5 times their diameter, Fig. 57. For plain joints either full or ring gaskets, Fig. 58 may be used.

56. Keys.—Keys of various forms are used to prevent relative motion between shaft and pulleys, gears, crank arms, etc. The saddle key shown at I in Fig. 59 is used when only a small force is to be transmitted and

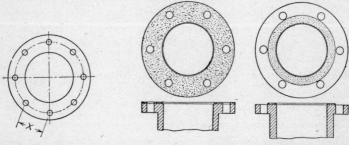

FIG. 57.   FIG. 58.   Full and Ring Gaskets.

where close or frequent adjustment is required. The flat key shown at II requires a flat spot on the shaft. Its holding power is a little greater than the preceding form. Set screws are sometimes used to secure closer

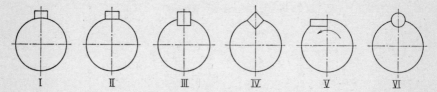

I   II   III   IV   V   VI

FIG. 59.   Forms of Keys.

contact. The square or rectangular form of key is most used. The sides should fit closely in the hub and shaft. Square keys, shown at III, are often made with $W = D/4$ in which W = width of key and D = diameter of shaft. Other proportions are $W = D/4$ and $T = D/6$ to $D/4$. Unwin gives $W = D/4 + 1/8''$ and $T = D/8 + 1/8''$. A different way of locating a square key is shown at IV.

57. For taper keys, the taper may be from $1/16''$ to $3/16''$ per foot of length. A practical standard is $1/8''$. Keys should be one half in the shaft and one half in the hub. When a large force is transmitted two keys placed 90° apart are used. The length of keys should be about one and one half times the diameter of the shaft.

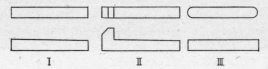

I   II   III

FIG. 60.   Plain, Gib, and Round End Keys.

TABLE 6. Dimensions of Keys

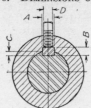

Shaft Diameter (Inclusive)	A	B	C	D	Shaft Diameter (Inclusive)	A	B	C	D
7/16 − 13/16	3/16	1/8	1/16	5/16	4½ − 5½	1¼	3/4	3/8	3/4
7/8 −1 5/16	1/4	3/16	3/32	3/8	5 9/16− 6½	1½	7/8	7/16	7/8
1 3/8 −1 3/4	3/8	1/4	1/8	1/2	6 9/16− 7½	1¾	1	1/2	7/8
1 3/16 −2¼	1/2	5/16	5/32	1/2	7 9/16− 8½	2	1¼	5/8	1
2 5/16 −2¾	5/8	3/8	3/16	5/8	8 9/16− 9½	2¼	1¼	5/8	1
2 13/16−3¼	3/4	1/2	1/4	5/8	9 9/16−10 15/16	2½	1½	3/4	1¼
3 5/16 −3¾	7/8	1/2	1/4	5/8	11 −12 15/16	3	1¾	7/8	1¼
3 13/16−4 7/16	1	5/8	5/16	3/4	13 −15	3½	2	1	1¼

TABLE 7. Standard Woodruff Keys

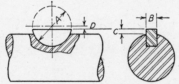

Woodruff Key.

Sizes Used		Dimensions									
Shaft Diameter	Key Numbers	Key No.	A	B	C	D	Key No.	A	B	C	D
5/16 − 3/8	1,	1	1/2	1/16	1/32	3/64	B	1	5/16	5/32	1/16
7/16 − 1/2	2, 4	2	1/2	3/32	3/64	3/64	16	1 1/8	3/16	3/32	5/64
9/16 − 5/8	3, 5	3	1/2	1/8	1/16	3/64	17	1 1/8	7/32	7/64	5/64
11/16− 3/4	3, 5, 7	4	5/8	3/32	3/64	1/16	18	1 1/8	1/4	1/8	5/64
13/16	6, 8	5	5/8	1/8	1/16	1/16	C	1 1/8	5/16	5/32	5/64
7/8 − 15/16	6, 8, 10	6	5/8	5/32	5/64	1/16	19	1 1/4	3/16	3/32	5/64
1	9, 11, 13	7	3/4	1/8	1/16	1/16	20	1 1/4	7/32	7/64	5/64
1 1/16 −1 1/8	9, 11, 13, 16	8	3/4	5/32	5/64	1/16	21	1 1/4	1/4	1/8	5/64
1 3/16	11, 13, 16	9	3/4	3/16	3/32	1/16	D	1 1/4	5/16	5/32	5/64
1 1/4 −1 5/16	12, 14, 17, 20	10	7/8	5/32	5/64	1/16	E	1 1/4	3/8	3/16	5/64
1 3/8 −1 7/16	14, 17, 20	11	7/8	3/16	3/32	1/16	22	1 3/8	1/4	1/8	3/32
1 1/2 −1 5/8	15, 18, 21, 24	12	7/8	7/32	7/64	1/16	23	1 3/8	5/16	5/32	3/32
1 11/16−1 3/4	18, 21, 24	A	7/8	1/4	1/8	1/16	F	1 3/8	3/8	3/32	3/32
1 13/16−2	23, 25	13	1	3/16	3/32	1/16	24	1 1/2	1/4	1/8	7/64
2 1/16 −2 1/2	25	14	1	7/32	7/64	1/16	25	1 1/2	5/16	5/32	7/64
....	....	15	1	1/4	1/8	1/16	G	1 1/2	3/8	3/16	7/64

The Lewis key is shown at V and the direction of the driving shaft is indicated. This key is in compression. A round key shown at VI is often a desirable form. The ordinary plain key is illustrated at I in Fig. 60, a key provided with a gib to make its removal easier is shown at II and a round end key at III. The third form is fitted into a shaft when it is desired to arrange for a part to slide on the shaft. When a long key is secured in a shaft and used in this way it is called a feather or feather key.

58. The Woodruff key, which consists of a part of a circular disc is shown in Table 7. The circular seating allows the key to assume the proper taper when a piece is put on the shaft. Data for various forms of keys is given in Tables 5 and 7.

59. Riveting.—Machines or structures composed entirely or in part, of sheet metal are fastened together by rivets, put into place red hot. Boilers, tanks, steel structures etc., are fastened together permanently in this way. Rivets are generally made of mild steel. They have a head on one end and sufficient length to allow forming a head on the other end after being put into place.

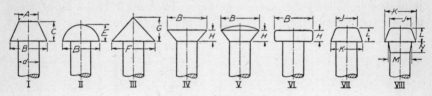

FIG. 61.   Rivet Heads.

60. Rivet Heads.—Forms of rivet heads are illustrated in Fig. 61 and dimensions are given in Table 8. The forms of heads are as follows: I Cone head, II Button head, III Steeple head, IV Flat countersunk head, V Oval countersunk head, VI Flat head, VII Pan head—straight neck, and VIII Pan head—swell neck. The information on rivet heads is from, "Scientific Facts," published by the Champion Rivet Co., Cleveland, Ohio.

61. Rivet Holes.—The holes for rivets may be either punched or drilled. As punching injures the metal, drilled holes are better for pressure work and are required for steam boiler work. The injury due to punching may be removed by annealing or the hole may be punched small and reamed to size. Holes are made $1/16''$ larger than the rivets used in them. Thus a rivet for a $1''$ hole is $15/16''$ diameter before driving.

62. Calking.—For many purposes rivets must make a leak tight

TABLE 8
DIMENSIONS OF RIVETS
(From "Scientific Facts," Champion Rivet Co.)

Diagram of Rivet	A	B	C	E	F	G	H	J	K	L	M	N
$1/2$	$15/32$	$7/8$	$7/16$	$3/8$	1	$9/16$	$1/4$	$1/2$	$13/16$	$3/8$	$9/16$	$1/4$
$9/16$	$17/32$	$63/64$	$1/2$	$27/64$	$1\,1/8$	$5/8$	$9/32$	$9/16$	$29/32$	$13/32$	$5/8$	$9/32$
$5/8$	$19/32$	$1\,3/32$	$35/64$	$15/32$	$1\,1/4$	$45/64$	$5/16$	$5/8$	1	$7/16$	$11/16$	$5/16$
$11/16$	$41/64$	$1\,13/64$	$39/64$	$33/64$	$1\,3/8$	$25/32$	$11/32$	$11/16$	$1\,3/32$	$15/32$	$3/4$	$11/32$
$3/4$	$45/64$	$1\,5/16$	$21/32$	$9/16$	$1\,1/2$	$27/32$	$3/8$	$3/4$	$1\,3/16$	$1/2$	$13/16$	$3/8$
$13/16$	$49/64$	$1\,27/64$	$23/32$	$39/64$	$1\,5/8$	$59/64$	$13/32$	$13/16$	$1\,1/4$	$17/32$	$7/8$	$13/32$
$7/8$	$53/64$	$1\,17/32$	$49/64$	$21/32$	$1\,3/4$	$63/64$	$7/16$	$7/8$	$1\,5/16$	$9/16$	$15/16$	$7/16$
$15/16$	$57/64$	$1\,41/64$	$53/64$	$45/64$	$1\,7/8$	$1\,3/64$	$15/32$	$15/16$	$1\,13/32$	$19/32$	1	$15/32$
1	$15/16$	$1\,3/4$	$7/8$	$3/4$	2	$1\,1/8$	$1/2$	1	$1\,1/2$	$5/8$	$1\,1/16$	$1/2$
$1\,1/16$	1	$1\,55/64$	$15/16$	$51/64$	$2\,1/8$	$1\,13/64$	$17/32$	$1\,1/16$	$1\,9/16$	$21/32$	$1\,1/8$	$17/32$
$1\,1/8$	$1\,1/16$	$1\,31/32$	$63/64$	$27/32$	$2\,1/4$	$1\,17/64$	$9/16$	$1\,1/8$	$1\,5/8$	$11/16$	$1\,3/16$	$9/16$
$1\,3/16$	$1\,7/64$	$2\,5/64$	$1\,3/64$	$57/64$	$2\,3/8$	$1\,21/64$	$19/32$	$1\,3/16$	$1\,3/4$	$23/32$	$1\,1/4$	$19/32$
$1\,1/4$	$1\,11/64$	$2\,3/16$	$1\,3/32$	$15/16$	$2\,1/2$	$1\,13/32$	$5/8$	$1\,1/4$	$1\,13/16$	$3/4$	$1\,5/16$	$5/8$
$1\,5/16$	$1\,15/64$	$2\,19/64$	$1\,9/64$	$63/64$	$2\,5/8$	$1\,15/32$	$21/32$	$1\,5/16$	$1\,15/16$	$25/32$	$1\,3/8$	$21/32$
$1\,3/8$	$1\,9/32$	$2\,13/32$	$1\,13/64$	$1\,1/32$	$2\,3/4$	$1\,35/64$	$11/16$	$1\,3/8$	2	$13/16$	$1\,7/16$	$11/16$
$1\,7/16$	$1\,11/32$	$2\,33/64$	$1\,17/64$	$1\,5/64$	$2\,7/8$	$1\,5/8$	$23/32$	$1\,7/16$	$2\,3/32$	$27/32$	$1\,1/2$	$23/32$
$1\,1/2$	$1\,13/32$	$2\,5/8$	$1\,5/16$	$1\,1/8$	3	$1\,11/16$	$3/4$	$1\,1/2$	$2\,3/16$	$7/8$	$1\,9/16$	$3/4$

joint as well as hold the plates together. To assist in this a blunt chisel is used to force or pound the edge of one of the plates down against

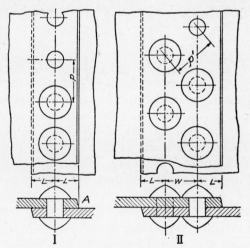

FIG. 62. Lap Joints.

another. This is called calking and makes a steam or water tight joint between the plates. The bevel of about 75° to 80° shown in Fig. 62 at A is to make calking easier.

63. Lap Joints.—A lap joint consists of two plates which lap over each other. When one row of rivets is used as at I in Fig. 62 it is called a single riveted lap joint. A double riveted joint is shown at II, Fig. 62.

The distance between the centers of two rivets in the same row is called *pitch*. The distance from the center line of the rivets to the edge of the plate is called *lap*. The lap is commonly made equal to one and one half times the diameter of the rivet. The distance from the center of a rivet in one line to the center of a rivet in the next line is called the diagonal pitch and may be found from the formula.

$$p' = \frac{2}{3}p + \frac{d}{3}.$$

Either *chain riveting*, Fig. 63, or *staggered riveting*, Fig. 64, may be used when there are several rows of rivets.

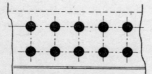
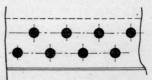

Fig. 63.   Chain Riveting.   Fig. 64.   Staggered Riveting.

64. Rivets which are put in place in the shop where the work is fabricated are called *shop rivets* and are represented as in Fig. 62.   Rivets

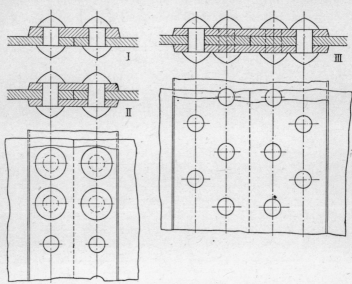

Fig. 65.   Butt Joints.

driven in the field or where the construction is put in place are called *field rivets* and are represented as in Figs. 63 and 64.

65. Butt Joints.—Three forms of butt joints are shown in Fig. 65. At I a single butt-strap having a thickness of about one and one fourth times the thickness of the plates is used. Single and double riveted joints with two butt-straps are shown at II and III. In such cases the butt-straps may be $1/16''$ thinner than the plates.

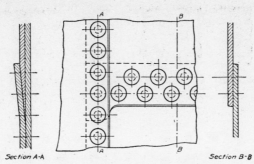

FIG. 66.   Joint for Three Plates.

66. When three plates come together they must be arranged so as to maintain a tight joint. One method is shown in Fig. 66 where one of the plates is thinned out.

67. Miscellaneous Connections.—Methods of making connections are shown in Fig. 67. Angles may be used as at I and IV or one of the

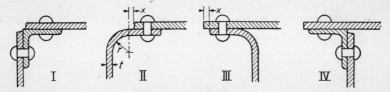

FIG. 67.   Connections.

plates may be bent as at II and III. In this case the radius of curvature *r* can be made about two and one half times the thickness of the plate.

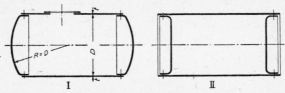

FIG. 68.   Cylindrical Tanks.

Also note that a short straight part x is provided to allow easy calking. When drawing to small scale, thin sections are sometimes blacked in as shown in Fig. 68 at I and II, which also illustrates methods of closing the ends of cylindrical tanks.   With rounded ends the radius of curvature can be taken equal to the diameter of the tank.

68. Rolled Steel Shapes.—For   many   constructions,   rolled   steel shapes are used.   The dimensions and weights as well as other informa-

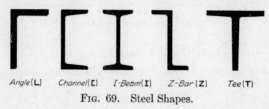

Angle(**L**)   Channel(**C**)   I-Beam(**I**)   Z-Bar (**Z**)   Tee(**T**)

Fig. 69.   Steel Shapes.

tion can best be obtained from the handbooks issued by the steel companies.   The names of a few of the common sections are given in Fig. 69.

The pitch of rivets for structural purposes may be taken at from three to six inches.   The distance from the center of the rivet to the edge of the plate should be about two times the rivet diameter.   The pitch for various sizes of rivets is given below.

MINIMUM RIVET SPACING

Diameter of rivet in inches	$^1/_4$	$^3/_8$	$^1/_2$	$^5/_8$	$^3/_4$	$^7/_8$	1
Pitch in inches	$^3/_4$	$1^1/_8$	$1^1/_2$	$1^7/_8$	$2^1/_4$	$2^5/_8$	3

The Osborn system of conventional representation of rivets is shown in Fig. 70.

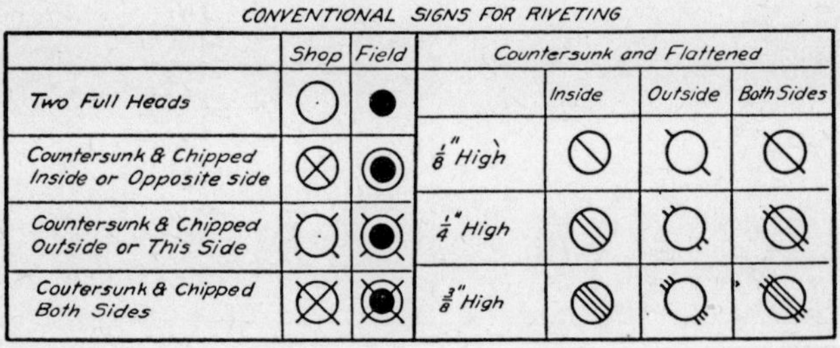

CONVENTIONAL SIGNS FOR RIVETING

	Shop	Field	Countersunk and Flattened			
				Inside	Outside	Both Sides
Two Full Heads	○	●				
Countersunk & Chipped Inside or Opposite side	⊗	◉	$^1/_8"$ High	⊘	◔	⊘
Countersunk & Chipped Outside or This Side	⊍	⊙	$^1/_4"$ High	⊘	◔	⊘
Coutersunk & Chipped Both Sides	⊗	⊗	$^3/_8"$ High	⊘	◔	⊘

Fig. 70.   Osborn Symbols.

69. Pins and Washers.—Pins used as fastenings are made in a large variety of forms, some of which are illustrated in Fig. 71.   They may be straight, taper, or split.

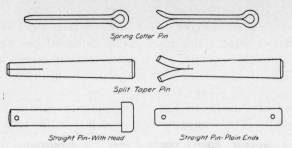

FIG. 71. Forms of Pins.

Dimensions for standard steel washers are given in Table 9. Cast iron washers, Fig. 72 may have proportions as follows:

$$A = d + \frac{1}{8}'', \qquad B = 3\frac{1}{2}d + \frac{1}{8}'', \qquad C = \frac{3}{4}d + \frac{1}{4}''.$$

FIG. 72. Cast Iron Washer.

TABLE 9

DIMENSIONS OF STANDARD STEEL WASHERS

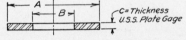

Bolt Diameter	A	B	C	Bolt Diameter	A	B	C
$\frac{3}{16}$	$\frac{1}{4}$	$\frac{9}{16}$	18	$1\frac{1}{8}$	$1\frac{1}{4}$	$2\frac{3}{4}$	9
$\frac{1}{4}$	$\frac{5}{16}$	$\frac{3}{4}$	16	$1\frac{1}{4}$	$1\frac{3}{8}$	3	8
$\frac{5}{16}$	$\frac{3}{8}$	$\frac{7}{8}$	16	$1\frac{3}{8}$	$1\frac{1}{2}$	$3\frac{1}{4}$	8
$\frac{3}{8}$	$\frac{7}{16}$	1	14	$1\frac{1}{2}$	$1\frac{5}{8}$	$3\frac{1}{2}$	8
$\frac{7}{16}$	$\frac{1}{2}$	$1\frac{1}{4}$	14	$1\frac{5}{8}$	$1\frac{3}{4}$	$3\frac{3}{4}$	8
$\frac{1}{2}$	$\frac{9}{16}$	$1\frac{3}{8}$	12	$1\frac{3}{4}$	$1\frac{7}{8}$	4	8
$\frac{9}{16}$	$\frac{5}{8}$	$1\frac{1}{2}$	12	$1\frac{7}{8}$	2	$4\frac{1}{4}$	8
$\frac{5}{8}$	$\frac{11}{16}$	$1\frac{3}{4}$	10	2	$2\frac{1}{8}$	$4\frac{1}{2}$	8
$\frac{3}{4}$	$\frac{13}{16}$	2	10	$2\frac{1}{4}$	$2\frac{3}{8}$	$4\frac{3}{4}$	5
$\frac{7}{8}$	$\frac{15}{16}$	$2\frac{1}{4}$	9	$2\frac{1}{2}$	$2\frac{5}{8}$	5	4
1	$1\frac{1}{16}$	$2\frac{1}{2}$	9	....			

Approx. Thick. $18 = \frac{1}{20}''$ $16 = \frac{1}{16}''$ $14 = \frac{5}{64}''$ $12 = \frac{7}{64}''$ $10 = \frac{9}{64}''$

$9 = \frac{5}{32}''$ $8 = \frac{11}{64}''$ $5 = \frac{7}{32}''$ $4 = \frac{15}{64}''$

CHAPTER III

MACHINE DRAWING

70. Working Drawings.—Any drawing used to give information and directions for doing work is a working drawing.

Such drawings are made by architects and civil, mechanical, and electrical engineers, for buildings, bridges, power plants, machine shops and all kinds of industrial work. This book treats of present practice in machine drawing.

71. There are two general classes of machine drawings—assembly drawings and detail drawings. These have been listed as follows:

A. Assembly drawings in outline or section. Design lay-out drawings. Erection Drawings. Skeleton or diagram drawings.

B. Assembly working drawings. Part assembly working drawings. Location drawings to show relation of parts with dependent dimensions and fits for two or more details. Tool, jig and fixture drawings.

C. Detail working drawings. General purpose drawings. Pattern drawings. Machine drawings. Forging drawings, Etc.

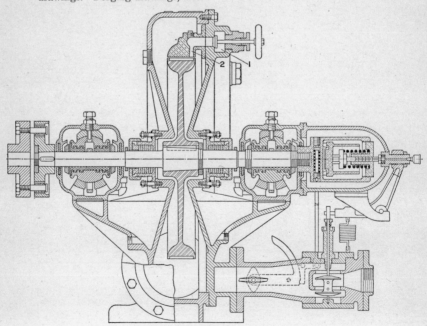

Fig. 73. Main Assembly Drawing.

38

72. A main assembly drawing of a B. F. Sturtevant Co., Type 6, Steam Turbine is shown in Fig. 73.

"Steam enters an annular steam chamber in the casing of the turbine through a balanced throttle valve (1). From this chamber it passes through nozzles (2) to the rotor or bucket wheel. These nozzles expand the steam to a pressure equal to the exhaust pressure in the turbine casing, so that the steam leaves the nozzles at a very high velocity.

"At this high velocity the steam then impinges against the semi-circular rotor buckets, imparting full impulse to the rotor, and leaves the buckets in the reverse direction. As it leaves the rotor, the steam enters the semi-circular reversing buckets, which are cast in one piece with the nozzles, which again reverse the direction of the steam and drive it back into the rotor. The steam enters and leaves the rotor in a circular motion several times before its kinetic energy is absorbed and its velocity dropped to that of the rotor. It then passes out into the exhaust."

73. Detail Drawings.—A detail drawing, Fig. 74 is one which contains the necessary views of each single piece, completely dimensioned and with specifications as to material, machining, etc.

1. Choose views which will completely describe the shape of the piece.
2. Do not draw unnecessary views.

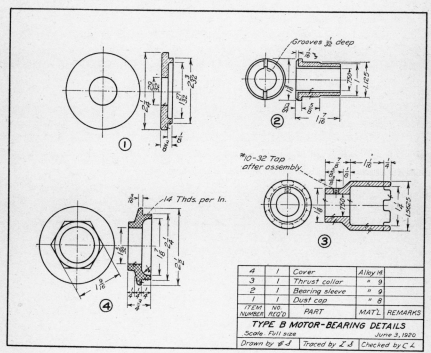

4	1	Cover	Alloy 14	
3	1	Thrust collar	" 9	
2	1	Bearing sleeve	" 9	
1	1	Dust cap	" 8	
ITEM NUMBER	NO. REQ'D	PART	MAT'L	REMARKS

TYPE B MOTOR-BEARING DETAILS
Scale · Full size   June 3, 1920
Drawn by *G S* | Traced by *I S* | Checked by *C L*

Fig. 74. A Detail Drawing.

3. Views should carry dimensions without crowding.

4. Choose a scale that will show the piece clearly.

5. Choose a scale that will not require crowding of dimensions.

6. Detail drawings are made full size, half size, quarter size or eighth size.

7. Avoid the use of different scales on same sheet when possible.

8. Arrange detail parts in the same position and order that they will have in the assembled machine when this is possible.

9. Keep views of each part near together but do not crowd them.

10. Leave a space between views of *different* pieces.

11. When possible, details that are closely related mechanically should be kept on the same sheet.

12. Make detail drawings so complete that no additional information will be required for duplicating the parts shown.

13. Small parts may be grouped together as: small castings; bronze and composition castings; forgings; bolts and screws, etc.

14. Standard small parts such as pressure gauges, oil and grease cups, lubricators, valves, ball bearings, etc., which can be described by notes can be drawn in outline or not at all.

15. If special or extra views of any kind are used, they must be defined by explanatory notes.

74. Making a Detail Drawing.—There are three major considerations when starting a detail drawing.

> (*a*)　Choice of Views,
> (*b*)　Treatment of Views,
> (*c*)　Choice of Scale.

A freehand layout sketch is very convenient and helpful, especially when standard size drawing sheets must be used.

First locate the main *center* and *base lines* for all views. Then draw the *preliminary blocking in* lines for all views. Finally work out the shape of the object.

75. Consider the object shown in Fig. 75. Two base lines and two center lines have been drawn at I in the order shown by the numbers. Note that the front view is located by the two base lines and that the top and end views are each located by one center line and one base line. At II the preliminary *"blocking in"* lines have been drawn very lightly, while at III, three of the final lines drawn distinctly have been added as their length is fixed. The "blocking in" is completed at IV. The details have been drawn at V and the preliminary lines have been gone over to give them the character of the other final lines.

The general procedure for pencil drawings is to block in with straight lines and large circles. The small circles and fillets are drawn last. If the drawing is not to be inked or traced, the dimension, extension, and section lines should be drawn very lightly and the figures and notes added.

76. Drawings are not often inked on paper as good pencil work serves

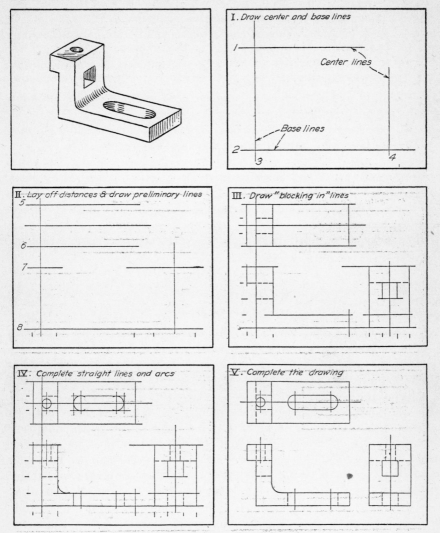

FIG. 75. Penciling a Detail Drawing.

just as well and requires less time. If many copies are wanted, tracing cloth is used. The ink will work better on the dull side, especially if it is first dusted with powdered chalk. For erasing either pencil or ink, use a pencil eraser. Pencil tracings are often made on tracing paper or cloth. If a thin bond paper is used, blue prints can be made from pencil drawings. The dimensions are often put on in ink. The order of inking is shown in Fig. 76, where fine lines are used to represent the pencil drawing.

77. The order of inking on either paper or cloth is:

1. Center lines.
2. Small circular arcs and circles.
3. Large circular arcs and circles.
4. Irregular curved lines.
5. Straight horizontal lines.
6. Straight vertical and slant lines.
7. Dotted circles and arcs.
8. Dotted straight lines.
9. Extension and dimension lines.
10. Dimensions, notes, title.
11. Section lining.

All inking except arrow points, figures and lettering must be done with the instruments and the order given must be followed if good drawings are to be made. Use Gillott's 404 pen for lettering, arrows, etc.

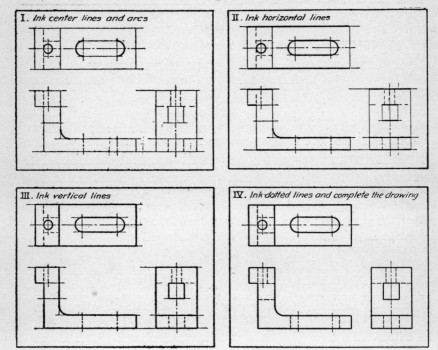

Fig. 76. Inking a Detail Drawing.

78. Blue Printing.—Blue prints are made on sensitized paper as follows:

Place a tracing with the inked side next to the glass of a printing frame, Fig. 77. Next place a piece of blue print paper on the tracing,

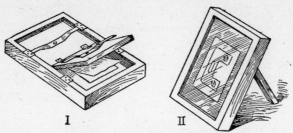

I   II

FIG. 77.   A Blue Print Frame.

coated side down.   Follow this with a felt pad and close the frame.   Expose to direct sunlight as indicated at II.· The length of exposure varies from 30 seconds in strong sunlight with rapid printing paper to three or four minutes under the same conditions with slow printing paper.   After exposing, the paper is removed and washed in clear water.   New paper has a yellow color on the coated side which changes to a gray-bronze after exposure.   Electric light is very generally used in large plants and for commercial blue printing.   Machines for this purpose as well as many other methods of duplication are described in drawing supply catalogs.

79. Assembly Drawings.—As already indicated, assembly drawings may be made for almost any purpose.   For showing the general appearance of a machine and giving center and overall dimensions an outline assembly such as Fig. 78 is used.

It is sometimes desirable to give all the dimensions on an assembly drawing so that the machine can be built from it.   This gives an assembly working drawing.   A part or group assembly drawing shows a group of parts in their relation to each other.   If dimensioned, no detail drawings are needed.

Piping or wiring diagrams are assembly drawings made to show the sizes, location and arrangement of pipes and wires.   When drawn to scale and completely dimensioned, they are called piping or wiring drawings.

Erection drawings show the order of putting parts together, dimensions for center distances, location of oil holes, valves, switches, etc.

80. Making an Assembly Drawing.—The purpose for which the drawing is desired must first be considered, after which the proper selection of views must be made. The next step is to determine the position of the views on the sheet and the scale to be used. The detail drawings are then collected ready for reference.

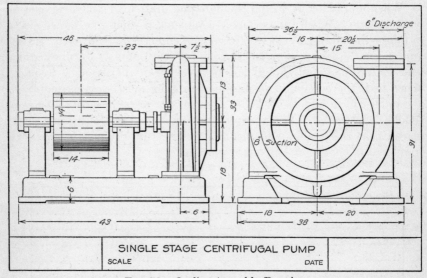

SINGLE STAGE CENTRIFUGAL PUMP

SCALE   DATE

Fig. 78.   Outline Assembly Drawing.

Locate the main center and base lines for the complete machine. Locate the center and base lines of the larger details of which the machine is composed. Draw the larger stationary parts in the different views. Determine limiting positions of moving parts if there are any. After this the smaller parts may be drawn very much in the same order as though assembling the actual machine. Since a small scale is often used, judgment must be exercised as to the amount of detail to be drawn. The character of the machine must show in the completed drawing. Maximum distances for stationary or moving parts, positions for foundation bolts, location of shafts, pulleys, piping and other dimensions having to do with erection or connecting up must be checked and are often given on the drawing.

81. Identification, Record, Etc.—For commercial engineering work, clean cut drawings having a definite character and containing all essential information are required. Extra views or notes, "fancy" lettering, complete detailing of standard parts to exact scale, confusion of dotted lines, and other non-essential work add to the cost of the drawing and to the cost of using the drawing.

Every piece drawn should have a name and a number so that it can be identified. The same name should always be used for a given part. The identification number for a part is generally put in a circle near the name of the part or the views representing it.

When a drawing is started the date and draftsman's name should be written on it. When the tracing is completed it should be signed either in full or by initials, by all who have worked on it, as draftsman, tracer, and checker, and by those responsible for its approval. Abbreviations lead to mistakes and should not be used when they can be avoided. When used the possibility of misunderstanding must be considered and a standard form adopted. When changes are made on a drawing they should be indicated. This is often done by enclosing a letter in a circle placed near the change and recorded in the title or record strip with statement of change and the date when made.

MATERIAL LIST

Part Number	Name of Part	No. Req'd.	Mat'l.	Pattern No.	Remarks
1	Emergency Valve	1	C.I.	M-932	
2	Valve Stem	1	Steel		
3	Stuffing Box Gland	1	C.I.	M-933	
4	Gland Stud	2	Steel		
5	Valve Liner	1	Tool Steel		
6	Bell Crank	1	Tool Steel		
7	Stud for No.6	1	Steel		
8	Split Pin for No.1	2	Steel		$\frac{3}{16}"\times 2"$

Fig. 79. Bill of Material.

Part lists should be complete, and numbers for patterns, tools and dies or other necessary information for identification or record should be placed on the drawing and recorded on filing cards or in record books.

BOLT LIST FOR 5"x6" STEAM ENGINE

No.	Name	No. Req'd	Diam.	Lgth.	Lgth. of Thread.	Material	No. Nuts	Location
1	Stud - Hex Nut	6	$\frac{5}{8}$	$2\frac{3}{8}$	$\frac{7}{8}$	Steel	6	Cyl. Hd. to Cyl.
2	Bolt - Hex Hd.	6	$\frac{5}{8}$	$2\frac{1}{2}$	$\frac{7}{8}$	Steel	—	Cyl. to Frame
3	Stud - Hex Nut	8	$\frac{5}{8}$	$2\frac{3}{8}$	$\frac{7}{8}$	Steel	8	Cover to Stm. Chest
4	Set Screw	2	$\frac{5}{8}$	$1\frac{1}{4}$	$1\frac{1}{4}$	Steel	—	Eccentric to Shaft
5	Bolt - Hex Hd & Nut	2	$\frac{1}{2}$	$4\frac{3}{4}$	$1\frac{1}{2}$	Steel	4	Eccentric

Fig. 80. Bolt List.

Every drawing should have a number and be recorded so as to be easily found. Systems of filing, numbering, recording, transmitting and keeping track of drawings vary with the kind of work, and the extent to which the drawings are used. Some forms are shown in Figs. 79, 80 and 81.

PIPE AND FITTINGS LIST

Size	Pipe Feet	Number of Valves	Number of Fittings	Threads	Material	Make
$\frac{1}{2}$	365			R	W.I.	
$1\frac{1}{4}$	185			R	W.I.	
$1\frac{1}{4}$		8 Globe		R	Brass	T-Z Co.
$1\frac{1}{4}$			21 Ells	R	C.I.	
$1\frac{1}{4}$			7 Tees	R	C.I.	
$1\frac{1}{4}$			5 Couplings	R & L	C.I.	

FIG. 81. Pipe and Fittings List.

82. Idioms of Drawing.—The basis for all working drawings is orthographic projection. For simple parts the regular views are used and all lines both full and dotted are drawn. There are many cases however when such representations might make it difficult to read the drawing, or require a long time to make the drawing. In the practical application of drawing it has been found necessary to depart from true projection under some conditions and to use special or idiomatic representations. Such conventional representations may be full views or sectional views, either partial or complete. A view of an object is not a picture and is not to be regarded as such, still we should be careful not to convey a false impression of an object or its construction. It is to avoid the possibility of such false impressions that various conventional representations have been developed. In the practice of engineering, time has ever been an important element, and conventions or representations of the more com-

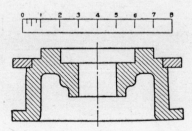

FIG. 82. Section without Dotted Lines.

mon parts of machinery have been devised to save time. The true projection of a screw thread would involve drawing a helix and when the
frequency with which screw threads occur is considered, the necessity
for using idioms or "engineering short hand" can be understood. There
are many other conditions where conventional treatment is desirable.

83. Treatment of Sectional Views.—It is not necessary to include all
dotted lines beyond the plane of a section if they tend to confuse rather
than help. In some cases only the sectioned surfaces and the full lines
beyond them are shown, Fig. 82. Whenever dotted lines tend to confuse, they should be left out, compare Figs. 83 and 84.

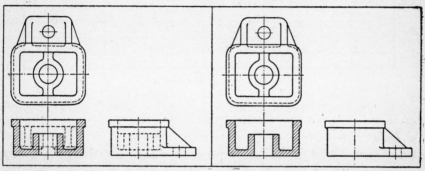

FIG. 83. Complete Section.   FIG. 84. Preferred Section.

When a sectional view is used in place of an exterior view, all of the
full lines beyond the plane of the section are generally drawn. In cases

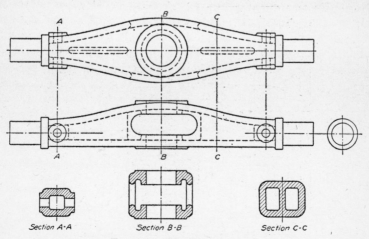

Section A·A   Section B·B   Section C·C

FIG. 85. "Sliced" Sections.

where the shape of the sectioned surface is the important feature or when the full lines beyond the cut surface require a great deal of time to draw without adding to the usefulness of the drawing, they should be left out as in Fig. 85, where several "sliced" sections are shown.

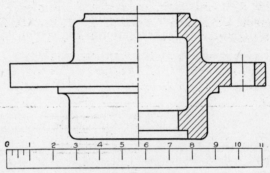

FIG. 86.   Half Section.

A view should serve the purpose for which it is intended without unnecessary or confusing lines.   Extra or part views are often sufficient.

84. It is sometimes desirable to show both the exterior and section in one view.   This can be done when the view is the same on both sides of a center line by drawing one half in section and the other half in full as in Fig. 86.   All or most all of the dotted lines are often omitted from both halves.   The planes of the section form a right angle and cut away one quarter of the object.   If two "half sectional" views are used they

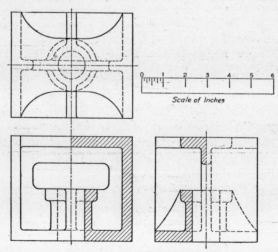

FIG. 87.   Two Half Sections.

should be cut by planes which will bring the two half sections toward each other as shown, Fig. 87.

85. When different pieces are shown in a section they are indicated by changing the direction of the cross hatching. The width of spacing between section lines is determined by the area to be sectioned, smaller areas having them closer together than larger ones. Different materials are sometimes indicated by different forms of section lining. Fig. 88

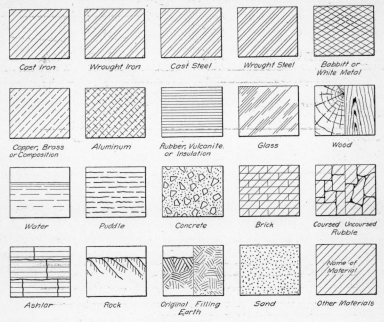

FIG. 88. A. S. M. E. Symbols for Sectioning.

gives the forms suggested by a Committee of the American Society of Mechanical Engineers. The spacing of lines shown will be found satisfactory for most areas. All lines must be fine, of uniform width and uniformly spaced. The character of sectioning must not be depended upon to tell the material and a note should always be added when the materials are not perfectly evident. Their chief value is to make it easier to distinguish different pieces.

86. Common Uses and Treatments of Sections.—There are many cases where parts of a view are not sectioned. Such parts as shafts, bolts, nuts, screws, rivets, keys, pulley arms, gear teeth, etc., are not sectioned even though the rest of the view is in section. This saves time and in many cases makes the drawing easier to read, Fig. 89.

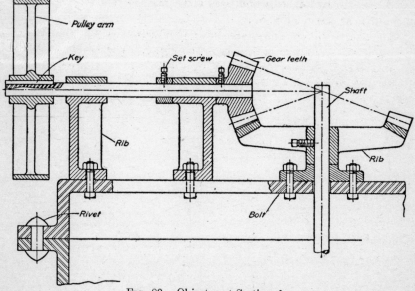

FIG. 89.   Objects not Sectioned.

A larger scale can often be used by "breaking" the piece, and moving the parts together.   The manner of breaking generally indicates the shape of the cross section and the material as in Fig. 90.   This method

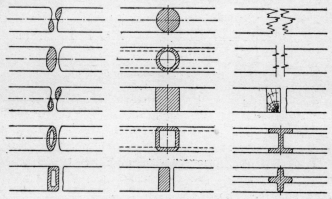

FIG. 90.   Revolved Sections.

cannot be used unless the cross section is uniform in shape, generally shown by a "set in" or revolved section.   The true taper is drawn when a long tapering piece is represented by the above method, Fig. 91.

87. Treatment of Ribs and Special Sections.—When a sectional view gives a false impression of solidity it is often modified. Ribs, pulley

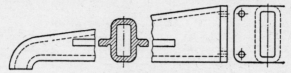

FIG. 91. Tapered Piece with Section.

arms, etc., are not sectioned for this reason, Fig. 92. Good practice requires the arms, ribs, etc., to be shown in their true length rather than

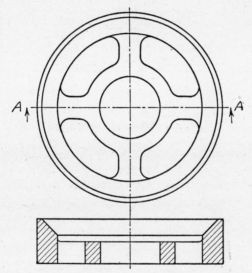

FIG. 92. Section through Rib.

as they would project. Fig. 93 at I is a true projection but better practice is shown at II.

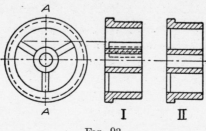

FIG. 93.

When a rib occurs on a plane of a section in such a way that it is necessary to call attention to it, alternate sectioning can be used as in

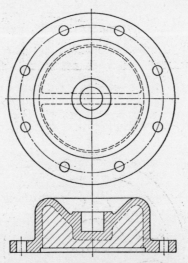

FIG. 94. "Alternate" Sectioning.

Fig. 94. Note the use of the dotted line to show the extent of the rib. This method can be used to advantage on one view drawings.

88. When small areas are sectioned the surfaces may be "blacked in" as in Fig. 95. When large areas are sectioned the surfaces may be in-

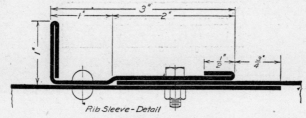

FIG. 95. "Blacked in" Section.

dicated by short lines following the contour lines, Fig. 96, sometimes called "herring bone" sectioning. Dotted sections are in the nature of

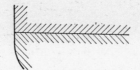

FIG. 96. "Herring bone" Section.

"phantom views" as shown in Fig. 97 where dotted section lines are

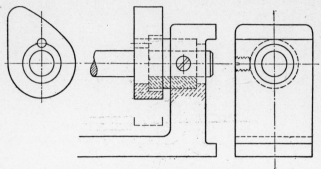

FIG. 97.   Dotted or "Phantom" Section.

used on a full view to distinguish different pieces.   This treatment
sometimes saves an extra view.

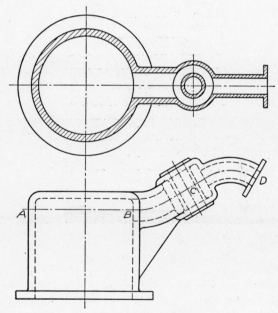

FIG. 98.   Developed Section.

A "developed section" is shown in Fig. 98, where the true length
of each part of the cutting plane shows in the sectional view.

89. Contour and Continuity.—The contour or characteristic appearance of an object is often an aid in the quick interpretation of a drawing. This is illustrated in Fig. 99, where the usual treatments for

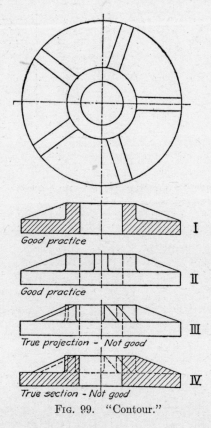

Fig. 99. "Contour."

exterior and sectional views are shown at I and II. The true projections are not only less useful but require more time to draw as indicated at III and IV.

The representation of a cylinder head in Fig. 100 is a similar case. A true section on plane A–A is shown at I. At II the section is taken on B–B and revolved into position of A–A. The bolt holes and lugs are then located at their true distances from the center. An alternate method is shown at III, where the section C–F is revolved.

90. Ribs, lugs, ears and other incidental parts are better left in full when they occur in a sectional view. The section of an object having an

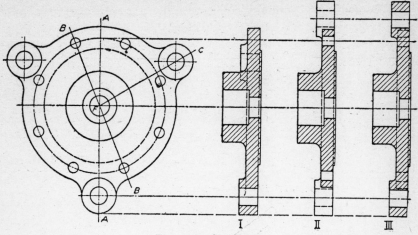

FIG. 100. Symmetry.

uneven number of incidental parts or having incidentals "off centers" is best shown as though there were an even number and near but not coincident with the plane of the section. The general rule of continuity is to section those parts which continue clear around the axis.

It is often desirable to show the contour elements of cylinders and cones unbroken when openings or attached parts would cause a break

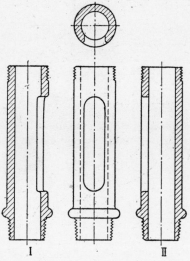

FIG. 101. "Contour."

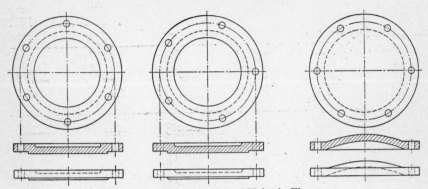

FIG. 102.   Representation of Holes in Flanges.

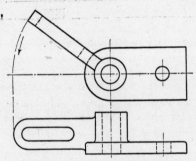

FIG. 103.   "True Length" View.

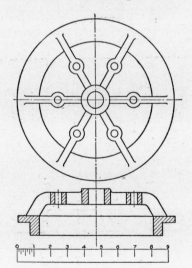

FIG. 104.   Conventional Treatment.

if shown in true projection. This treatment is illustrated in Fig. 101 in which the true section is shown at I and the conventional treatment at II.

91. There are many cases where true projection is departed from in the interest of simplicity and clearness.

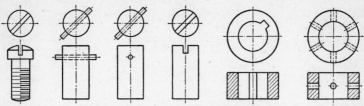

FIG. 105. Conventional Treatment.

The section or edge view of a flange shows the centers of the bolt holes a distance apart equal to the diameter of the circle of drilling, regardless of their true projection. In such cases the intermediate holes are not drawn as they add nothing to the information conveyed by the drawing. Several treatments for drilled flanges are indicated in Fig. 102.

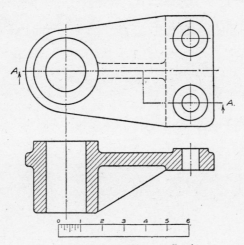

FIG. 106. Non-continuous Section.

92. Special Views.—When an object has one part at an angle the two views do not have to project if a better representation may be obtained by revolving or developing one of the views or part of a view. In Fig. 103 the top view shows the true angle and the front view the true shape of the left hand part of the object, by revolving it parallel to the vertical plane.   Auxiliary views or parts of views are often convenient.

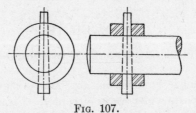

Fig. 107.

Some studies in representation are given in Figs. 104 to 108 which show both exterior and sectional treatments.   The line marked in Fig. 108 is not an actual line but is useful for reading the drawing.   Special

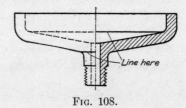

Fig. 108.

views and idiomatic representations have come about in the practical use of drawing as an engineering language.   They have been adopted through custom because they convey the idea more clearly and exactly, or more quickly than strict conformity to the rules of projection would do.

CHAPTER IV

PRINCIPLES AND PRACTICE OF DIMENSIONING

93. Dimensioning.—Dimensions are figures placed on drawings to tell the size of the parts which are represented. As generally considered, dimensioning also includes specification as to degree of accuracy, kind of finish, materials, number of parts, etc. To dimension a drawing successfully the construction of the patterns, methods of machining, fitting and putting together of the machine must be studied.

94. Notation of Dimensioning.—The notation of dimensioning consists of lines and symbols used on a drawing to show the application of figures and notes to describe the size of a machine or part.

The dimensioning of a drawing is never started until all the views are complete, thus finishing the description of shape. Following this, extension and dimension lines are drawn to indicate the location of dimensions. Finally the arrow points, figures and notes are put on, using a lettering pen such as Gillott's 404.

A *dimension line*, Fig. 109, indicates a distance, the amount of which is shown by a figure placed in a space left in the dimension line.

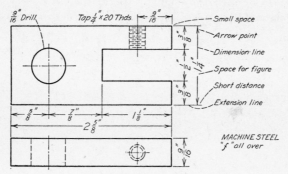

FIG. 109. Notation of Dimensioning.

Arrow-heads or *points* are used at the ends of a dimension line to show the extent of a dimension. An arrow point very much enlarged is shown in Fig. 110. Note that it is two and one half times as long as it is wide and that the two sides are slightly curved.

Extension lines are used to extend lines of a view when a dimension line is placed outside of the view. A small space is always left between an extension line and the object line, Fig. 109. The extension line extends a small distance beyond the arrow point.

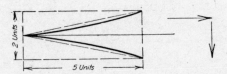

Fig. 110. The Arrow Point.

Pointing or *leading* lines are very fine, full or dash lines drawn from a figure or note to show the part of the drawing to which the figure or note applies. They may be left plain, have an arrow point, or preferably half an arrow point. Fig. 111.

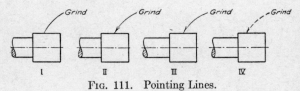

Fig. 111. Pointing Lines.

95. Surfaces which are machined are said to be "finished" and are indicated on a drawing by marking the line which represents the edge view of the surface with a symbol "f" shown enlarged in Fig. 112.

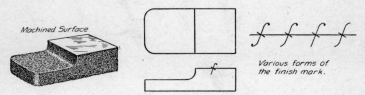

Fig. 112. The Finish Mark.

Feet are indicated by the mark (′) and inches by (″) as 5′–3″. When all dimensions are given in inches the inch marks are often omitted. The figures should be placed so as to read from the lower and right hand sides of the sheet and in line with the dimension lines, Fig. 109.

96. Elements of Dimensioning.—A definite method of dimensioning can be followed by separating constructions into parts. These parts can be divided into geometrical solids. Each of the solids can be dimensioned and their relations to each other fixed by location dimensions. Thus, there are two kinds of dimensions to be considered.

1. Size dimensions,
2. Location dimensions.

97. The following six cases contain the elements of dimensioning and can be applied to most objects, Fig. 113.

The *first case* is the prism and modifications of the prism. The length, breadth, and thickness are required. Two of these are given

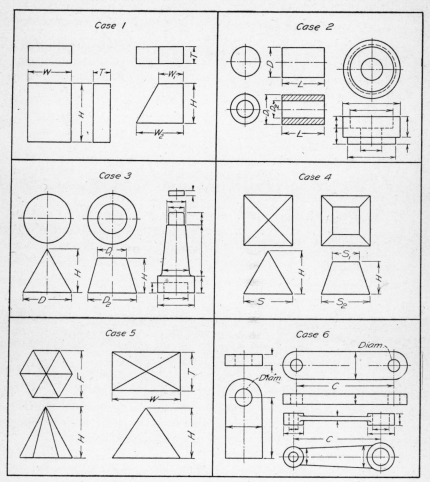

FIG. 113.   Elements of Dimensioning—The Six Cases.

on one view and the third on one of the other views.   In general dimensions are placed between views rather than to one side.

The *second case* is the cylinder, where the diameter and length are given on one view.

The *third case* is the cone and similar shapes where the dimensions are given on one view.

The *fourth case* is the square pyramid and similar shapes where the dimensions are given on one view.

The *fifth case* is any kind of pyramid where two views are used for dimensions.

The *sixth case* is "rounded end" parts where center distances are given.

98. Systems of Dimensioning.—There are four general systems of dimensioning as follows (Fig. 114):

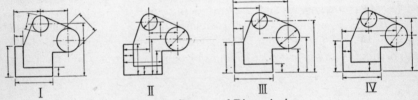

Fig. 114.   Systems of Dimensioning.

I. All figures outside of the object lines.

II. All figures inside of the object lines.

III. All figures given from two reference or base lines at right angles to each other.

IV. A combination of the preceding systems.

The first system is favored as the dimension lines and figures are kept separate from the interior and allow details to be easily seen.   The size and shape are separated.

The second system may be used when there is little detail within the view.   It preserves the outline of the view but often there is confusion due to the crossing of the lines and crowding of figures.

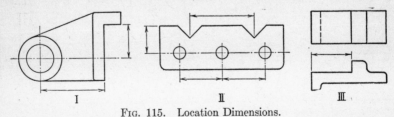

Fig. 115.   Location Dimensions.

The third system is particularly adapted to plate work and laying out where holes must be accurately located.

The fourth system is the one generally used but making it conform to the first system by placing dimensions outside whenever *conveniently* possible.

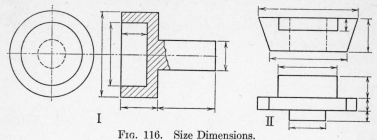

I   II

FIG. 116.   Size Dimensions.

Location dimensions are illustrated in Fig. 115, size dimensions in Fig. 116 and the application of the elements in Fig. 117.   Note the similar position of dimensions, that each elementary part is dimensioned and its position fixed with respect to another part or reference line by a loca-

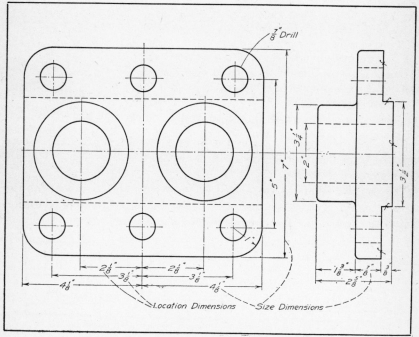

FIG. 117.   Elements of Dimensioning Applied.

tion dimension where needed. The location dimension for cylindrical and similar parts is given from the axis of the cylinder.

99. Location of Dimensions.—Facility in manufacture should be a motto in dimensioning. The figures must be so placed as to be easily found and perfectly clear in their meaning when found. Consider the effect of location upon ease of reading the drawing. It is very seldom necessary to repeat dimensions. Drilling is generally best located in the view where it shows in plan, that is, in the view where it is laid out. The drilling for flanges is dimensioned by giving the diameter of the bolt circle and the size of bolt holes. The holes are understood to be equally spaced unless otherwise noted.

Dimension lines must be kept away from other lines and from each other. The clear distance between lines should be from $3/16''$ to $5/16''$, estimated. If there are several parallel lines they should be the same distance apart. Larger dimensions should be kept outside of smaller ones. In the interest of clearness there should be as few lines as possible crossing each other. Similar pieces should be dimensioned in exactly the same way.

100. When a slanting dimension line must be used, the figure reads in

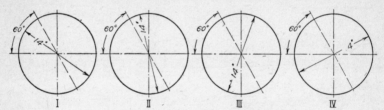

FIG. 118. Slanting Dimension Lines.

line with the slant, either from the left or right as in Fig. 118 where the limiting angle is shown as 60°.

When a dimension line is made continuous for several successive dimensions as in Fig. 119, it is said to be continuous.

When the dimension lines for several successive dimensions are not continuous, they are said to be "staggered," Fig. 120.

FIG. 119. "Continuous" or "Chain" Dimensions.

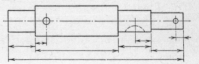

FIG. 120. "Staggered" Dimensions.

101. Methods of Finishing.—Kinds of finished surfaces should be indicated by a note as in Fig. 121. The meaning of the different shop

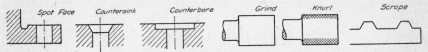

FIG. 121.   Kinds of Finished Surfaces.

operations involved should be found by consulting a good shop hand-book.   Holes should be marked according to how they are to be formed or treated as: Core; Drill; Bore; Punch; Ream; Tap; Counter bore; Countersink, etc.   Surfaces should be marked to tell the shop operations to be performed as: Finished; Rough Finish; Chipped; Spot Faced; Scraped; Ground; Polished; Filed; etc.

The kind of fit is sometimes marked as Loose Fit; Running Fit; Driving Fit; Forced or Pressed Fit; Shrink Fit; etc.   The tendency of present practice is to give the tolerance or limits of accuracy required.

102. Dimensioning Arcs and Curves.—A number of cases of dimensioning arcs and curves are illustrated in Fig. 122.   If a complete circle

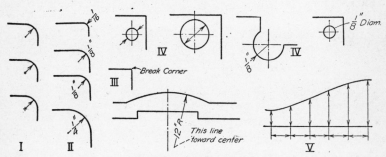

FIG. 122.   Arcs and Curves.

is shown, give the diameter in preference to the radius.   For arcs and fillets give the radius.   If desired, the center for a radius may be indicated by one of the methods shown at I.   For a very small radius the figure may be placed as at II.   The note "break corner" at III means that the sharp corner is to be removed so that it will be slightly rounded. The dimension line for an arc should always take a direction which would pass through the center as shown in the figures.   The methods at IV may be used for small diameters.   For other curves a templet may be called for, or shown full size on the sheet.   Another method is to give a number of parallel dimensions and the distance between them as at V.

103. Dimensioning Angles and Tapers.—Angles are generally dimensioned by giving the number of degrees included between the two sides. Three methods of dimensioning angles are shown in Fig. 123. For many

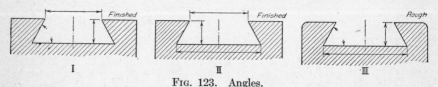

FIG. 123. Angles.

purposes standard tapers are used, in which the name and number of the taper is given in a note. This fixes all necessary dimensions as given in tables for B. & S. (Brown & Sharpe); Morse; Read Lathe Center; Jarno, and Sellers Tapers. Sometimes a note is employed giving the taper per inch or per foot of length, as $3/4''$ *per foot.* When the slope is considerable it may be given as a ratio, as 1:1, indicating a 45° slope. When fillets or rounds come at the ends of inclined lines the methods of Fig. 124 at, I,

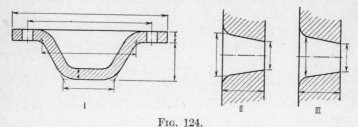

FIG. 124.

II, and III are used. The larger diameter at III although located inside gives the same dimension as at II. The dimensions indicate the distances between the sloping lines where they cut the vertical lines.

104. Dimensioning in Crowded Places.—A drawing should be made to a scale sufficiently large to carry most of the dimensions without crowding. It is not always possible to avoid a few somewhat crowded dimensions. Notes and figures may be placed out of their usual positions when necessary. Some methods to use in such cases to preserve clearness are shown in Fig. 125.

105. Dimensioning Shafts and Cylindrical Pieces.—Shafts should be dimensioned by giving the diameters and lengths together with the sizes of keyways and pins and their location, Fig. 126. Often the size dimensions both detail and overall are given below the view and the location dimensions above.

Examples of dimensioning for shafts and similar conditions are shown in Fig. 127. The position of bearings is sometimes shown by diagonal

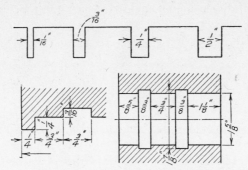

FIG. 125. "Crowded" Dimensions.

lines, either plain or "blacked in." A square section may be shown in a similar way. A note should be used in either case if necessary to make the meaning clear. Positions of pulleys, gears, etc., are located by center lines as in the drawing, Fig. 183.

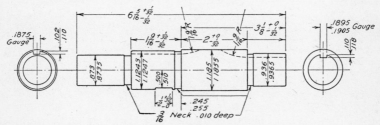

FIG. 126. A Shaft Drawing.

106. Dimensioning Wood Constructions.—Such wood constructions as the engineer has to do with seldom require such close dimensions as are common for metal machinery. Timbers are located by centers, and are dimensioned by note as 2 x 4; 4 x 6; etc. Sometimes with the

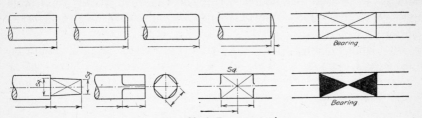

FIG. 127. Shaft Representations.

length added as $2'' \times 8'' - 6' - 10''$. Boards are specified by note as $1'' \times 10''$; $^3/_4'' \times 6''$ etc. Such sizes are nominal rather than exact as a $2'' \times 4''$ piece may measure $1^3/_4'' \times 3^3/_4''$, etc. General overall dimensions should be given and any other dimensions which must come to a required figure. Wood foundation timbers; crib work; shelves; wall and ceiling planks to support or hold machines, pulleys, etc., and similar mechanical uses of wood must be drawn and dimensioned by the mechanical draftsman, Fig. 128. Nails, screws, bolts, etc., are specified in notes.

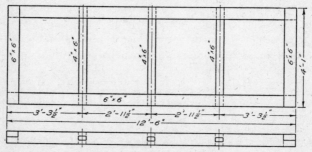

FIG. 128. Dimensioning Wood.

Nails are specified by a number followed by the letter d. 8 d means 100 nails weigh 8 lbs. and is read 8 penny.

107. Dimensioning for Interchangeable Manufacture.—The whole question of limits, fits, tolerance, manufacturing equipment of machines, tools, jigs, fixtures, etc., is involved in properly dimensioning a drawing for parts which are to be interchangeable. It is not necessary that limits be given for every dimension but only for those which are required because of the relation of parts. Some dimensions should be given without limits especially when particular accuracy is not required. Giving limits for all dimensions frequently makes the specification ambiguous as where several part dimensions are each given limits and the overall dimension is also given limits as in Fig. 129. The separate dimensions might be within the limits but the overall might not be, as a great number of combinations of part dimensions is possible. Fig. 130 is the correct method where several dimensions are given limits. In such cases take all measurements from the same surface. The dimensioning of drawings for interchangeable manufacture is well treated in a series of articles by Earle Buckingham, starting in the July 1919 number of "Machinery," Industrial Press, New York, from which the following is quoted. The complete article should be studied by those having to do with interchangeability.

108. "The problem of the proper dimensioning of component drawings is strictly a mathematical one.   There are a few basic principles in regard to it which are as fixed and simple as Newton's three laws of motion, but are even more difficult at times to apply correctly.   Whenever either of the two following principles is violated, trouble will inevitably follow:

"(1) In interchangeable manufacturing, there is but one dimension (or group of dimensions) in the same straight line that can be controlled within fixed tolerances.   That is the distance between the cutting surface of the tool and the locating or registering surface of the part being machined.   Hence, it is incorrect to locate any point or surface with tolerances from more than one point in the same straight line.

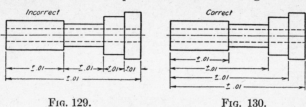

Fig. 129.   Fig. 130.
Limit Dimensions.

"(2) Dimensions should be given between those points which it is essential to hold in a specific relation to each other.   The majority of dimensions, however, are relatively unimportant in this respect.   It is good practice to establish locating points in each plane, and to give, as far as possible, all such dimensions from these common locating points.

"There are also a few other general principles which it is good practice to follow.   Although violations of them are not errors in themselves, they lead to many unnecessary errors.   In all of this work we must realize that we cannot create anything that is altogether fool-proof; the best we can hope to accomplish is to make conditions such that little or no excuse remains for making a mistake.   The three following principles are of this order.

"(1) The basic dimensions given on component drawings for interchangeable parts should be the maximum metal sizes, except for force fits and other unusual conditions.   The direct comparison of the basic sizes are the most important cases.   It is evident that these sizes are the most important ones, as they control the interchangeability.   They should be the first determined and, once established, they should remain fixed if the mechanism functions properly and the design is unchanged.   The direction of the tolerances, then, would be such as would increase this clearance. For force fits, such as taper keys, etc., the basic dimensions should be those which determine the minimum interference (which is the 'danger zone' in this case) and the direction of the tolerances for this class of work should be such as would increase this interference.

"(2) Dimensions should not be duplicated between the same points. The duplication of dimensions causes much needless trouble, due to changes being made in one place and not in others. It causes less trouble to search a drawing to find dimensions than it does to have them duplicated and, though more readily found, inconsistent.

"(3) As far as possible, the dimensions on companion parts should be given from the same relative locations. This procedure assists in detecting interferences and other improper conditions.

"If careful thought is given to these component drawings, much time and effort will be saved later in the shop. If they are neglected, all the future work will suffer. A large percentage of the mistakes made in the manufacturing departments may be traced back to improper component drawings."

109. General Rules.—Some rules and practice not included in the preceding articles are here collected.

For a complete drawing: give sizes of pieces for the patternmaker; give sizes and finish for the machinist; give assembly dimensions; give office dimensions; give notes where needed.

Always dimension similar parts in the same way.

Give dimensions from finished surfaces or to center lines. When a piece is symmetrical, the dimension is given "about" or across the center line, as at I, Fig. 131. Methods shown at II and III are sometimes used.

Place dimensions so that other dimensions or lines do not cross them or crowd them. Where a number of dimension lines are parallel do not place the figures under each other but locate as in Fig. 132.

"Overall" dimensions should be given when necessary as at I, Fig. 133. For the piece shown at II, *do not* give overall dimension but give "center to center" dimension.

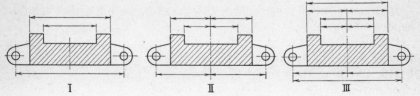

I   II   III

Fig. 131. Dimensioning "About" and "Across" Center Lines.

When most of the dimensions are in inches, they may all be given in inches and the mark ($''$) omitted.

When feet and inches are used, always indicate by the mark ($'$) and

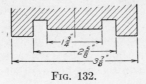

FIG. 132.

($''$) or by (ft.) and (in.).   Decimals may have the point emphasized by writing thus 1.$''$05.

Center lines and object lines have only one purpose and should never be used as dimension lines.

On structural drawings, dimension lines are made continuous and the figure is placed above the line.

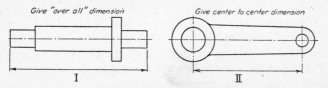

FIG. 133.   "Over-all" and "Center to Center" Dimensions.

Where clearness is not sacrificed, parts can sometimes be defined in one view by using a note to give missing dimensions or to specify diameters, etc.

Small details which are standardized do not have to be completely dimensioned.   This is true for bolts and screws, standard tapers, piping, wire, sheet metal, rope, chain, pins, rolled steel shapes, etc.   See "Machinery" or "American Machinist" Handbooks.   A valuable article on "How Machinery Materials and Supplies are Sized" is given in "Machinery," February, 1916.

Do not put notes within the views if it can be avoided.   Keep notes clear of all lines.

In general, put all notes referring to the same piece together and near the view of that piece.

Use pointing lines whenever they will make the reading of the drawing easier or where the application of a note might be doubtful.

110. Checking Drawings.—The checking of a drawing is one of the important duties of most draftsmen.   Whenever possible it should be done by someone who has not worked on the drawing.   In the drafting room a blue pencil is used for checking if the tracing is marked.   For some drawings a "check print" is made from the tracing and used.   A white, red, or yellow pencil is used on the blueprint.   Sometimes one color is used for what is O K and another to make corrections or changes. For school drawings, a soft lead pencil is satisfactory.

The first thing to do is to see if the drawing can be used without unnecessary difficulty, and to see if the parts are such as will fit together and operate successfully.

There must be sufficient views to completely determine the parts.

All necessary dimensions for making the patterns, machining and erecting must be given and properly located.

Details and dimensions must be shown without crowding.   This requires proper choice of scale.

All figures must be checked for correctness by use of the scale and by computation.

All notes must contain a clear statement and be carefully located.

Notes containing the same meaning should be worded in the same way.

The materials of which the parts are made should be specified.

The construction of the patterns, cores, and methods of machining must be considered.

All finished surfaces must be indicated.   The kind of finish and accuracy required must be specified.

Limits or tolerance, must be given for dimensions where necessary.

Basic or starting surfaces and center lines must be located.

Standard parts must be used where possible.

The fewest number of different sizes of bolts and similar small parts should be specified.

There must be clearance for moving parts.

The name of each piece and the number required for a single machine or unit should be given on detail drawings.

CHAPTER V

MACHINE DETAILS

111. Machine Operations.—The parts of machines which come from the foundry, forge, or rolling mill, generally require finishing such as machining to size, drilling and tapping of holes, etc., before they can be assembled in the machine where they are to be used. A knowledge of what is involved in the processes of machining is important to the machine draftsman.

The principal operations are turning, drilling, boring, planing and milling. The machines used are lathes, drills, boring mills, planers, shapers, milling machines, etc. At least one book on machine shop practice should be studied while pursuing a course in machine drawing. The advertising pages of such magazines as "Machinery" and "American Machinist" are further sources of information which should not be neglected. Every opportunity should be availed of to observe and study work as it is carried out in the pattern shop, forge, foundry and machine shop. Such knowledge is invaluable and will often enable the draftsman to reduce the expense of production by simplifying or adapting his designs.

There are many details which are used on a great variety of machines. Parts which are used for similar purposes on different kinds of machines have many features that are common to all such parts. In order for a machine to have "character" it is necessary for the designer to have a knowledge of what has been done by other designers and to be familiar with the ordinary standard details of machines.

112. Graphical Data and Dimensions.—So much information is now given by graphical diagrams that their use must be understood by those who have to do with engineering matters. Charts serve to present

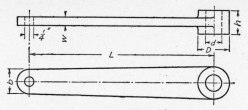

Fig. 134. Lever Dimensions.

73

information and to work out information as to power, forces, motions, and dimensions. Formulas and tables are often put into graphical form. When the curve is a straight line its slope can be figured from the equation for a straight line, $y = mx + b$, in which y is the ordinate, x is the abscissa, m is a ratio and b is a constant. Other equations may be worked out from curved lines if formulas are desired. Sometimes the dimensions

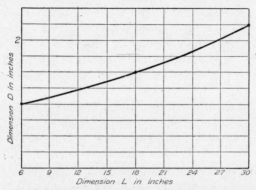

FIG. 135. Dimensions from Curve.

for two or three sizes of a machine part will be figured and plotted and the dimensions for other sizes within the range of the curve obtained from

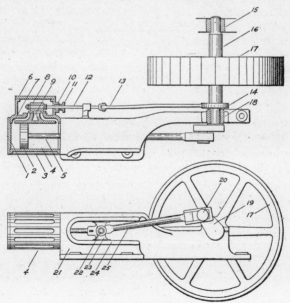

FIG. 136. Engine Details.

the graphical chart. This is illustrated in Figs. 134 and 135. The dimensions for three sizes of the lever are known as follows:

L	6	18	30
h	$^3/_4$	$^3/_4$	$^3/_4$
d	$^1/_2$	$^3/_4$	$1^1/_8$
D	1	$1^1/_2$	$2^1/_4$
W	$^1/_4$	$^1/_4$	$^1/_4$
b	$^3/_4$	$^3/_4$	$^3/_4$

Plot values of D for the three values of L and draw a curve as shown. Values of D for other values of L may be taken from the curve. Thus for 27″ length the value of $D = 2″$ and since $d = D/2$ we have $d = 1″$. The other dimensions are constant for all sizes.

113. Engine Details.—Steam engine details are typical of many machine parts. The names of the principal parts are given in connection with Fig. 136.

1. Cylinder head.
2. Piston.
3. Casing or lagging strip.
4. Cylinder.
5. Piston rod.
6. Steam chest cover.
7. Steam port.
8. Slide valve.
9. Exhaust port.
10. Valve rod stuffing box.
11. Valve rod gland.
12. Valve rod.
13. Eccentric rod.
14. Eccentric.
15. Outer bearing.
16. Main shaft.
17. Fly wheel.
18. Inner bearing.
19. Crank.
20. Crank pin.
21. Frame.
22. Crosshead pin.
23. Crosshead.
24. Crosshead guide.
25. Connecting rod.

Steam is admitted to alternate sides of the piston by means of the slide valve which is actuated by the eccentric through the eccentric rod. The piston transmits the pressure of the steam through the piston rod, crosshead, and connecting rod to the crank. The crank causes the shaft to revolve, carrying with it the flywheel, from which power may be transmitted by means of a belt.

114. Pistons are used in many kinds of machines and vary accordingly. A one-part piston is shown in Fig. 137. The names of the parts for a follower type piston are given for Fig. 138 as follows: 1, Piston Body; 2, Follower; 3, Follower Bolts; 4, Bull Ring; 5, Packing Rings. To prevent loss of pressure by leakage past the piston some form of packing ring is used. Pistons are generally made of cast iron, as are the rings.

The rings are turned to a slightly larger diameter than the cylinder, a piece is then cut out, and the rings sprung into place.   They are often

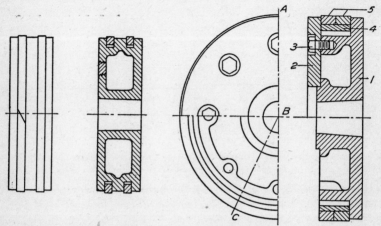

FIG. 137.   One Part Piston.   FIG. 138.   Piston and Follower.

made with eccentric diameters Fig. 139 with the cut on the thin side. The cut may be diagonal or lap, as in the figure.

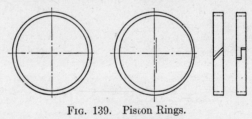

FIG. 139.   Piston Rings.

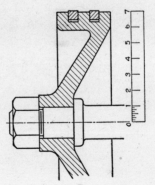

FIG. 140.   Locomotive Piston.

A form of locomotive piston is shown in Fig. 140. It is a steel casting for lightness and of conical form for strength. A gas engine piston is illustrated in Fig. 141.

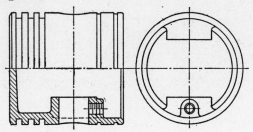

FIG. 141. Gas Engine Piston.

115. Crossheads are used on steam engines, pumps, air compressors and many other machines. Two types of crossheads are shown in Figs. 142 and 143, with the names of the parts. The body of the cross-

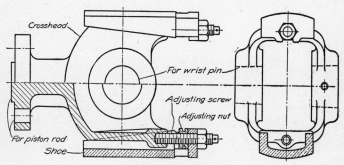

FIG. 142. Crosshead.

head is made of cast iron or steel and the gib or shoe of brass or may be babbitted.

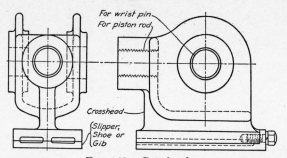

FIG. 143. Crosshead.

116. A connecting rod is used to connect a sliding part of a machine with a rotating part. They are made of wrought iron, steel, and brass. Forms vary greatly. The ends may be solid or open. Some provision

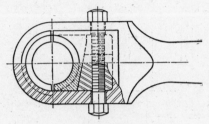

Fig. 144.   Connecting Rod End.

is generally made for adjusting the distance between the centers of the ends. The rod itself may have a circular, elliptical, rectangular, I-

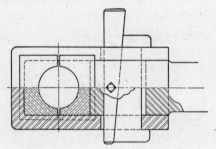

Fig. 145.   Connecting Rod End.

shape, or other form of cross section. Types of connecting rod ends are shown in Figs. 144, 145 and 146.

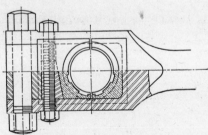

Fig. 146.   Connecting Rod End.

117. An eccentric is a circular disc which rotates about an axis which does not pass through its center, Fig. 147. An eccentric as made for

FIG. 147.   Eccentric.

use on a steam engine to move the steam valve is shown in Fig. 148.   It
consists of the eccentric, eccentric straps and bolts.   The eccentric is

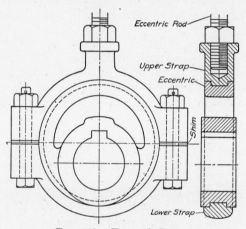

FIG. 148.   Eccentric Parts.

secured to a shaft which causes it to rotate and so move the eccentric
rod, which is attached to the straps.

118. A crank is a machine part which rotates about an axis near one
end.   It may be a part of the shaft or made separate and secured in
place.   A crank disc, overhung crank, and center crank, are shown in
Fig. 149 at I, II and III, where some general proportions are indicated.

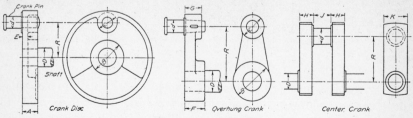

FIG. 149.   Cranks.

119. Levers, Handles, Etc.—Levers, handles and similar parts are used on a great variety of machines and are made in forms to suit their purpose, Fig. 150.

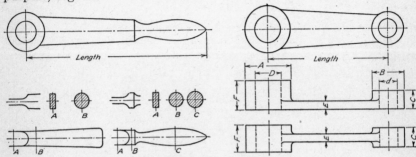

FIG. 150. Levers and Handles.

The length of a lever is from center to center of holes or an equivalent distance as illustrated.

The three classes of levers are shown in Fig. 151. In each case the

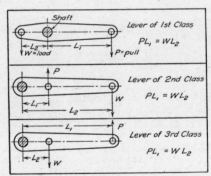

FIG. 151. Classes of Levers.

values for the loads or distances can be figured from the formulas.

$$PL_1 = WL_2 \quad P = \frac{WL_2}{L_1} \quad L_1 = \frac{WL_2}{P} \quad W = \frac{PL_1}{L_2} \quad L_2 = \frac{PL_1}{W}.$$

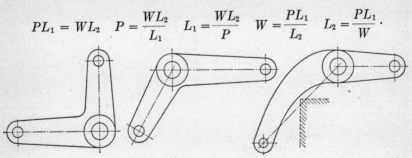

FIG. 152. Bell Cranks and Bent Lever.

When the load and force act at an angle some form of bell crank is used, Fig. 152. Bent levers are used when it is necessary to avoid a stationary part as shown. The length of a bent lever is the shortest distance between the two centers.

Handles are designed to suit a given position and so as to be convenient for getting hold of and operating. Several forms of machine tool handles are shown in Figs. 153 and 154 with standard dimensions as manufactured by The Cincinnatti Ball Crank Co. (Tables 10 and 11).

TABLE 10
MACHINE HANDLES AND TWO BALL LEVERS
(Cincinnati Ball Crank Co.)

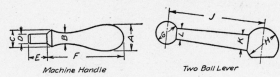

Machine Handle   Two Ball Lever

FIG. 153. Machine Handles.

Size	A	B	C	D	E	F	G	H	J	K	L
000......	$^7/_{16}$	$^3/_{16}$	$^5/_{16}$	.252 .253	$^7/_{16}$	$1^9/_{32}$	......	......	......	......	......
00......	$^5/_8$	$^5/_{16}$	$^5/_8$	.252 .253	$^7/_{16}$	$1^{15}/_{32}$	......	......	......	......	......
0......	$^3/_4$	$^3/_8$	$^9/_{16}$	.3145 .3155	$^7/_{16}$	$1^{23}/_{32}$	......	......	......	......	......
$^1/_2$....	$^{13}/_{16}$	$^5/_{16}$	$^1/_2$	.3145 .3155	$^7/_{16}$	2	......	......	......	......	......
1......	$^7/_8$	$^3/_8$	$^9/_{16}$	.377 .378	$^9/_{16}$	$2^1/_8$	$^3/_4$	$1^1/_8$	$2^9/_{16}$	$^1/_2$	$^3/_8$
$1^1/_2$....	......	......	......	......	......	......	$^{13}/_{16}$	$1^1/_4$	$2^{15}/_{16}$	$^9/_{16}$	$^7/_{16}$
2......	1	$^7/_{16}$	$^{11}/_{16}$	.4395 .4405	$^{11}/_{16}$	$2^3/_8$	$^{15}/_{16}$	$1^3/_8$	$3^{11}/_{32}$	$^9/_{16}$	$^7/_{16}$
3......	$1^1/_8$	$^7/_{16}$	$^{11}/_{16}$	.4395 .4405	$^{11}/_{16}$	$2^3/_4$	1	$1^1/_2$	$3^3/_4$	$^{11}/_{16}$	$^{15}/_{32}$
4......	$1^3/_{16}$	$^1/_2$	$^3/_4$	.4395 .4405	$^{11}/_{16}$	$3^7/_{32}$	1	$1^1/_2$	$4^1/_4$	$^3/_4$	$^1/_2$
5......	$1^3/_{16}$	$^1/_2$	$^3/_4$	.4395 .4405	$^{13}/_{16}$	$3^7/_{16}$	......	......	......	......	......
6......	$1^1/_4$	$^1/_2$	$^7/_8$	.503 .504	$^{15}/_{16}$	$3^5/_8$	1	$1^3/_4$	$5^1/_8$	$^3/_4$	$^1/_2$
7......	$1^3/_8$	$^1/_2$	$^{15}/_{16}$	.503 .504	$^{15}/_{16}$	$4^1/_{16}$	1	$1^3/_4$	$5^5/_8$	$^{25}/_{32}$	$^1/_2$
8......	$1^1/_2$	$^5/_8$	$1^1/_8$	.628 .629	$1^3/_{16}$	$4^9/_{16}$	1	$1^3/_4$	$6^1/_8$	$^{13}/_{16}$	$^{17}/_{32}$
10.....	......	......	......	......	......	......	$1^1/_8$	$1^3/_4$	$7^1/_{16}$	$^{13}/_{16}$	$^{19}/_{32}$
11.....	......	......	......	......	......	......	$1^3/_{16}$	$1^3/_4$	$7^{17}/_{32}$	$^7/_8$	$^5/_8$

TABLE 11

Ball Crank and Compound Rest Handles

(Cincinnati Ball Crank Co.)

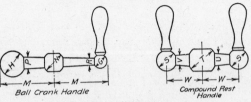

Fig. 154. Machine Handles.

Size	Size of Handle		G	H	M	N	P	R	S	T	U	V	W
	Ball Crank	Compound Rest											
0...	00	1	$5/8$	1	$1\,1/2$	$7/8$	$1/2$	$3/8$	$5/8$	$13/16$	$3/8$	$5/16$	$15/16$
1...	0	....	$3/4$	$1\,1/8$	$1\,3/4$	1	$1/2$	$3/8$	$3/4$	$1\,1/16$	$13/32$	$13/32$	$7/8$
$1\,1/2$.	$1/2$	....	$13/16$	$1\,1/4$	2	$1\,1/8$	$9/16$	$7/16$	.....	....	....	....	....
2...	1	2	$15/16$	$1\,3/8$	$2\,1/4$	$1\,1/4$	$9/16$	$7/16$	$3/4$	$1\,1/16$	$13/32$	$13/32$	$7/8$
3...	2	2	1	$1\,1/2$	$2\,1/2$	$1\,5/16$	$11/16$	$15/32$	$3/4$	$1\,1/16$	$13/32$	$13/32$	$7/8$
4...	2	....	1	$1\,1/2$	$2\,3/4$	$1\,5/16$	$23/32$	$1/2$	$3/4$	$1\,1/16$	$7/16$	$3/8$	$1\,1/8$
5...	3	2	1	$1\,5/8$	3	$1\,3/8$	$3/4$	$1/2$	$3/4$	$1\,1/16$	$7/16$	$3/8$	$1\,1/8$
6...	4	2	1	$1\,5/8$	$3\,1/4$	$1\,3/8$	$3/4$	$1/2$	$3/4$	$1\,1/16$	$7/16$	$3/8$	$1\,1/8$
7...	4	....	1	$1\,3/4$	$3\,1/2$	$1\,7/16$	$25/32$	$1/2$	$3/4$	$1\,1/16$	$7/16$	$13/32$	$1\,3/8$
8...	4	3	1	$1\,3/4$	$3\,3/4$	$1\,1/2$	$25/32$	$17/32$	$3/4$	$1\,1/16$	$7/16$	$13/32$	$1\,3/8$
9...	4	3	$1\,1/16$	$1\,3/4$	4	$1\,1/2$	$27/32$	$17/32$	$3/4$	$1\,1/16$	$7/16$	$13/32$	$1\,3/8$
10...	5	....	$1\,1/8$	$1\,3/4$	$4\,1/4$	$1\,9/16$	$13/16$	$19/32$	$7/8$	$1\,3/16$	$17/32$	$7/16$	$1\,9/16$
11...	5	4	$1\,3/16$	$1\,3/4$	$4\,1/2$	$1\,5/8$	$7/8$	$9/16$	$7/8$	$1\,3/16$	$17/32$	$7/16$	$1\,9/16$
12...	7	4	$1\,1/4$	2	$5\,1/2$	$1\,13/16$	$31/32$	$5/8$	$7/8$	$1\,3/16$	$17/32$	$7/16$	$1\,9/16$
13...	7	....	$1\,1/4$	2	$6\,1/2$	$1\,15/16$	$1\,1/32$	$23/32$	$1\,1/16$	$1\,3/8$	$5/8$	$1/2$	$1\,11/16$

120. Stuffing Boxes.—Common forms of gland stuffing boxes and screw stuffing boxes are shown in Figs. 155 and 156.

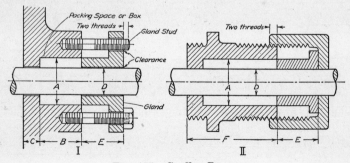

Fig. 155. Stuffing Boxes.

The gland stuffing box is used for rods $1\frac{1}{2}''$ and more in diameter. The names of the parts are given on Fig. 155. The box should be deep enough for at least four strands of packing and the gland proportioned so

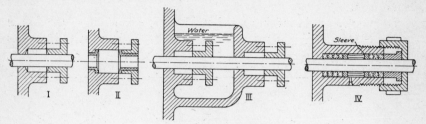

FIG. 156. Stuffing Boxes.

as to compress it to about one half its original length. The box and gland may be either flat or bevelled. If lined with composition the lining should be at least $\frac{3}{16}''$ thick, but for small rods (less than $2''$ diameter) it is generally advisable to make the gland either all brass or cast iron. The gland is moved by turning the nuts on the studs.

For rods $1\frac{1}{4}''$ diameter or less the common screw stuffing box, is much used. It is made of brass or composition except on very cheap work where cast iron is used.

Some general proportions for use with Fig. 155 are as follows: $A = 1.4D + .4''$, $B = .8D + .8''$, $C = \frac{1}{4}D + \frac{1}{4}''$ or more, $E = .8D + .8''$, $F = 2.5D + 1''$.

These are the common types, but the student should investigate and make sketches of some of the metallic packings as they are much used in good designs.

121. Fillets, Rounds, Arcs, Etc.—The suggestions which follow are to facilitate the drafting part of design and are not rules which must be strictly adhered to.

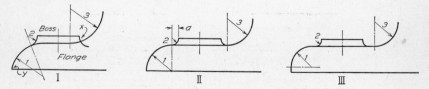

FIG. 157. Limiting Radii, Fillets and Rounds.

Fillets and rounds are so common that they should be understood. A part of a machine is shown at Fig. 157. The centers and radii are indicated. All the radii at I are too large, particularly those marked

1 and 2.   Radius 1 gives a point at y.   Radius 2 is so large that it cannot
be used for the complete circumference of the boss indicated at x.   Of
course a changing radius of fillet might be used, but this would not be as
good design.

The limiting radii are indicated at II while a much better design is
shown at III.   Note that the radii 1 and 2 are less than the thickness of

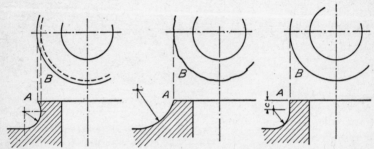

Fig. 158.   Effect of Different Fillets.

the flange and boss respectively.   The effect of a quarter circle is obtained by this method in which the flange and boss each start with a
straight line.

The effect of different fillets is shown in Fig. 158.   At I there is an
undercutting, at II the radius is too large, giving an irregular outline to
the top view, while the correct design is shown at III.

When arcs and straight lines are used the faults shown at a, Fig.
159, should be avoided.   Do not run an arc past the tangent point.   The
correct methods are shown at b.

122. Flanges.—Flanges for two bolts or nuts may take a variety of

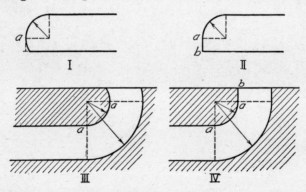

Fig. 159.   Tangent Points.

outlines other than circular as shown in Fig. 160. After locating the
centers of the bolt holes the extent of the flange may be found by adding

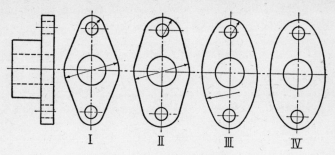

FIG. 160.   Flange Outlines.

twice the bolt diameter to the distance between bolt centers. The outline is often obtained as at I where the radius is equal to the diameter
of the hole, with center as shown. A better design is to use a radius
of one and one half the bolt hole diameter as at II. Either straight,
circular or elliptical lines may be used to complete the outline.

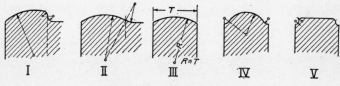

FIG. 161.   Flange Edges.

The edges are often finished with curves so as to avoid machining as
indicated in Fig. 161.

CHAPTER VI

BEARINGS, PULLEYS, ETC.

123. Bearings.—The motion of machine parts is generally either translation or rotation. Supports for moving parts are called bearings when the moving parts rotate. For translatory motion the supports are called guides.

The simplest form of support for a rotating member is a hole through a piece of metal. The rotating member is called a shaft or journal. A solid bearing is shown at I, Fig. 162. The shaft may rotate about a vertical axis as at II, in which case the support is called a step bearing.

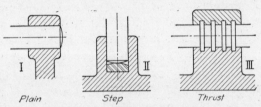

Plain   *Step*   *Thrust*

FIG. 162. Bearings.

The bearing shown at III is designed to prevent endwise motion by means of collars which run in spaces provided in the bearing. This is called a thrust bearing.

124. Smoothness of surfaces is only relative. Surfaces in contact wear rapidly so that it is necessary to provide for lubrication and for taking up the wear. For this reason the bearing is generally made in two parts. When this is not done a ring of metal called a bushing is fitted into the bearing and may be replaced when worn. Divided bushings are used when the bearing is made in two parts. Such bushings are called shells or boxes.

125. Bearing Metals.—For low pressures cast iron may be used but at high pressures and speeds it is liable to "seize" as the heat cannot be

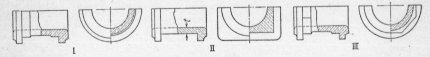

FIG. 163. Bearing Boxes.

dissipated fast enough. For this reason other metals are used such as brass, various white metals and babbitt. Babbitt metal is softer than

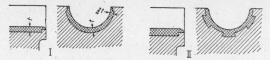

FIG. 164. Babbitted Boxes.

brass, flows more easily under pressure, and if heated will melt without seizing. Its frictional resistance is low so that it makes a good material

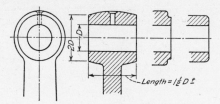

FIG. 165. Solid Bearing.

to use. It is too weak to support a load so it has to be held in place by shells of brass or cast iron which are provided with anchorage grooves. The babbitt may be melted and poured into the shell, using the shaft to mould it to the right size. For better work a smaller shaft is used and

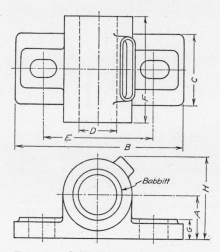

FIG. 166. Solid Babbitted Bearing.

the babbitt is peened into firm contact with the shell after which it is bored and scraped to size.

126. Various forms of brass and white metal boxes are suggested in Fig. 163. The thickness t may be made about $(d + 1.5)/12$ where d equals diameter of shaft. Babbitted boxes are indicated in Fig. 164 with some methods of supporting the babbitt. The thickness t may be made about $(d + 1)/12$ where d equals diameter of shaft.

127. Simple Bearings.—For a simple solid bearing the proportions of Fig. 165 may be used. Some dimensions for a babbitted bearing, Fig.

TABLE 12 (Fig. 166)

SOLID BABBITTED BEARING

Size of Shaft, Inches	A	B	C	E	F	G	H	Bolts	
								No.	Size
$^{15}/_{16}$ and 1	$1^1/_8$	5	2	$3^3/_8$	3	$^9/_{16}$	$2^1/_8$	2	$^1/_2$
$1^3/_{16}$ and $1^1/_4$.......	$1^3/_8$	$5^1/_2$	$2^1/_4$	$3^5/_8$	$3^3/_8$	$^5/_8$	$2^3/_4$	2	$^1/_2$
$1^7/_{16}$ and $1^1/_2$.......	$1^1/_2$	6	$2^9/_{16}$	4	$3^7/_8$	$^{11}/_{16}$	$2^3/_4$	2	$^1/_2$
$1^{11}/_{16}$ and $1^3/_4$.......	$1^{13}/_{16}$	$6^1/_2$	$2^3/_4$	$4^3/_8$	$4^1/_4$	$^5/_8$	$3^3/_8$	2	$^5/_8$
$1^{15}/_{16}$ and 2	$1^{11}/_{16}$	7	3	$4^3/_4$	$4^1/_2$	$^7/_8$	$3^7/_8$	2	$^5/_8$
$2^3/_{16}$ and $2^1/_4$......	$2^1/_8$	$7^5/_8$	$3^1/_4$	$5^1/_4$	$4^{11}/_{16}$	$^7/_8$	4	2	$^5/_8$
$2^7/_{16}$ and $2^1/_2$.......	$2^1/_8$	8	$3^1/_2$	$5^3/_4$	$5^7/_{16}$	$^{13}/_{16}$	$4^1/_4$	2	$^5/_8$
$2^{11}/_{16}$ and $2^3/_4$.......	$2^3/_8$	$9^3/_8$	$3^5/_8$	$6^1/_2$	$5^3/_4$	$^{15}/_{16}$	$4^3/_4$	2	$^3/_4$
$2^{15}/_{16}$ and 3	$2^1/_2$	$10^1/_2$	4	$7^3/_8$	$6^1/_8$	1	$4^7/_8$	2	$^3/_4$

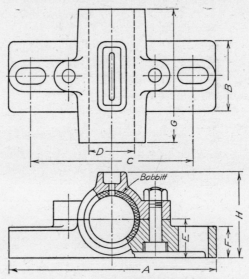

FIG. 167. Split Babbitted Bearing.

166 are given in Table 12. A split babbitted bearing is given in Fig. 167 with some dimensions in Table 13. The data in tables 12 to 16 is from the Royersford Foundry and Machine Company.

TABLE 13 (Fig. 167)

Split Babbitted Bearing

Size of Shaft, Inches	A	B	C	E	F	G	H	Bolts	
								No.	Size
$3/4$	$4^1/2$	1^1 $_4$	$3^3/8$	$5/8$	$1/2$	$2^1/16$	$1^1/2$	2	$3/8$
$7/8$	$4^1/2$	$1^1/4$	$3^3/8$	$5/8$	$1/2$	$2^1/16$	$1^1/2$	2	$3/8$
$15/16$	5	$1^3/8$	$3^3/4$	$3/4$	$5/8$	$2^1/2$	$1^3/4$	2	$3/8$
1	5	$1^3/8$	$3^3/4$	$3/4$	$5/8$	$2^1/2$	$1^3/4$	2	$3/8$
$1^1/8$	$5^1/2$	$1^5/8$	$4^1/4$	$15/16$	$3/4$	$2^7/8$	$2^1/4$	2	$3/8$
$1^3/16$ and $1^1/4$.......	$5^1/2$	$1^5/8$	$4^1/4$	$15/16$	$3/4$	$2^7/8$	$2^1/4$	2	$3/8$
$1^5/16$	$6^1/8$	$1^{15}/16$	$4^{11}/16$	$1^1/16$	$7/8$	$3^{11}/16$	$2^3/8$	2	$3/8$
$1^7/16$ and $1^1/2$.......	$6^1/8$	$1^{15}/16$	$4^{11}/16$	$1^1/16$	$7/8$	$3^{11}/16$	$2^3/8$	2	$3/8$
$1^{11}/16$ and $1^3/4$......	$6^7/8$	$2^5/16$	$5^3/16$	$1^5/16$	1	$4^5/16$	$2^7/8$	2	$1/2$
$1^{15}/16$ and 2	$7^1/2$	$2^5/8$	$5^7/8$	$1^1/2$	$1^1/16$	$4^{15}/16$	$3^1/4$	2	$1/2$
$2^3/16$ and $2^1/4$.......	$8^3/8$	$2^7/8$	$6^1/2$	$1^{11}/16$	$1^1/4$	$5^9/16$	$3^7/8$	2	$5/8$
$2^7/16$ and $2^1/2$.......	$9^1/4$	$3^1/8$	$7^3/8$	$1^{13}/16$	$1^3/8$	$6^1/8$	$4^3/16$	2	$5/8$
$2^{11}/16$ and $2^3/4$......	$10^1/4$	$3^1/2$	$8^1/8$	2	$1^1/2$	$6^{13}/16$	$4^3/8$	2	$3/4$
$2^{15}/16$ and 3	$11^3/16$	$3^3/4$	$8^7/8$	$2^3/16$	$1^9/16$	$7^7/16$	$4^5/8$	2	$3/4$

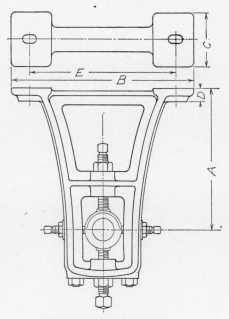

Fig. 168. Hanger Bearing.

128. Hangers.—Bearings for line shafting are supported by some form of hanger with provision for adjusting the position of the bearing. The general appearance and some proportions are shown in Fig. 168 (Table 14). A section of a ring oiled babbitted box for shafting is shown in Fig. 169. A rigid post box is illustrated in Fig. 170 (Table 15).

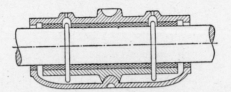

Fig. 169.　Section of Box.

129. Pulleys.—The forms and proportions of pulleys are dependent upon their use. For belt drives pulleys of cast iron, wood or steel are used with flat belts made of leather, cotton, rubber and other flexible materials.

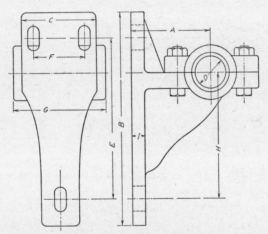

Fig. 170.　A Rigid Post Box.

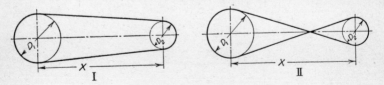

Fig. 171.　Length of Belt.

TABLE 14 (Fig. 168)

Universal Ring Oiling Hangers

Size of Shaft Inches	Drop A	L'ng'h of Boxes	B	C	D	E	F	Bolts No.	Size
$^{15}/_{16}$ and 1	10 to 12	$4^3/_4$	$13^1/_4$	4	1	$9^7/_8$	......	2	$^1/_2$
$1^3/_{16}$ and $1^1/_4$.......	14 to 16	$5^{13}/_{16}$	17	$4^3/_4$	1	$13^3/_8$	......	2	$^5/_8$
$1^7/_{16}$ and $1^1/_2$.......	14 to 16	$6^5/_8$	17	$4^3/_4$	1	$13^3/_8$	......	2	$^5/_8$
$1^{11}/_{16}$ and $1^3/_4$.......	16 to 18	$7^{13}/_{16}$	20	5	1	16	......	2	$^5/_8$
$1^{15}/_{16}$ and 2	16 to 18	$8^3/_8$	20	5	1	16	......	2	$^5/_8$
$2^3/_{16}$ and $2^1/_4$.......	18 to 20	$9^5/_8$	$22^1/_2$	6	$1^1/_4$	$18^1/_4$	......	2	$^3/_4$
$2^7/_{16}$ and $2^1/_2$.......	18 to 20	$10^5/_{16}$	$22^1/_2$	6	$1^1/_4$	$18^1/_4$	......	2	$^3/_4$
$2^{11}/_{16}$ and $2^3/_4$.......	18 to 20	$11^1/_2$	$23^1/_4$	7	$1^1/_2$	$18^3/_8$	......	2	1
$2^{15}/_{16}$ and 3	18 to 20	12	$23^1/_4$	7	$1^1/_2$	$18^3/_8$	......	2	1
$3^3/_{16}$ and $3^1/_4$.......	22 to 24	$13^1/_2$	$28^1/_2$	$10^3/_8$	$1^3/_4$	$23^1/_4$	$4^3/_4$	4	$^3/_4$
$3^7/_{16}$ and $3^1/_2$.......	22 to 24	$14^1/_2$	$28^1/_2$	$10^3/_8$	$1^3/_4$	$23^1/_4$	$4^3/_4$	4	$^3/_4$
$3^{11}/_{16}$ and $3^3/_4$.......	22 to 24	$15^1/_4$	$28^1/_2$	$10^1/_2$	$1^7/_8$	$22^1/_2$	$4^1/_4$	4	$^7/_8$
$3^{15}/_{16}$ and 4	22 to 24	$16^3/_8$	$28^1/_2$	$10^1/_2$	$1^7/_8$	$22^1/_2$	$4^1/_4$	4	$^7/_8$

TABLE 15 (Fig. 170)

Rigid Post Boxes

Size of Shaft, Inches	A	B	C	I	E	F	H	G	Bolts No.	Size
$^{15}/_{16}$ and 1	$3^7/_8$	$7^5/_{16}$	3	$^5/_8$	5	$1^7/_8$	$3^7/_8$	$3^1/_8$	3	$^1/_2$
$1^3/_{16}$ and $1^1/_4$....	$3^7/_8$	$8^1/_2$	$3^1/_4$	$^5/_8$	$6^1/_8$	$2^1/_4$	$4^7/_8$	$3^3/_4$	3	$^1/_2$
$1^7/_{16}$ and $1^1/_2$....	$3^7/_8$	10	$3^5/_8$	$^5/_8$	$7^1/_2$	$2^1/_2$	$5^7/_8$	$4^1/_2$	3	$^1/_2$
$1^{11}/_{16}$ and $1^3/_4$....	$5^7/_8$	$11^3/_8$	4	$^5/_8$	$8^3/_4$	$2^5/_8$	$6^7/_8$	$5^1/_4$	3	$^1/_2$
$1^{15}/_{16}$ and 2	$5^7/_8$	13	$4^3/_4$	$^3/_4$	10	3	$7^7/_8$	6	3	$^5/_8$
$2^3/_{16}$ and $2^1/_4$....	$5^7/_8$	$14^3/_4$	$5^1/_4$	$^3/_4$	$11^1/_8$	$3^1/_4$	$8^7/_8$	$6^3/_4$	3	$^5/_8$
$2^7/_{16}$ and $2^1/_2$....	$5^7/_8$	$16^1/_4$	$5^3/_4$	$^7/_8$	$12^1/_4$	$3^1/_2$	$9^7/_8$	$7^1/_2$	3	$^3/_4$
$2^{11}/_{16}$ and $2^3/_4$....	$5^7/_8$	$16^3/_4$	$6^5/_8$	$^7/_8$	$12^3/_4$	$3^3/_4$	10	$8^1/_4$	3	$^3/_4$
$2^{15}/_{16}$ and 3	$5^7/_8$	$19^1/_4$	7	1	15	4	$11^3/_4$	9	3	$^3/_4$

130. Belt Length.—The length of a belt for a pair of pulleys is best obtained by direct measurement, using a steel tape. For open belts, Fig. 171 at I, the length of belt may be calculated from the formula,

$$L = .131(D_1 + D_2) + \sqrt{X^2 + (D_1 - D_2)^2}.$$

For crossed belts as at II, the formula is:

$$L = .131(D_1 + D_2) + \sqrt{X^2 + (D_1 + D_2)^2};$$

L = length of belt in feet,
X = distance between centers in feet,
D_1 = diameter large pulley in inches,
D_2 = diameter small pulley in inches.

131. A graphical method of finding the length of belt for cone pulleys is given in the American Society of Mechanical Engineers Transactions, Vol. X. Given R_1 and R_2 and distance between centers C, Fig. 172.

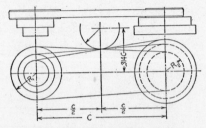

FIG. 172. Cone Pulley Radii.

Draw circles with radii R_1 and R_2 and a line tangent to them. At middle point of C erect a perpendicular and locate a point on it, .314 C above center line. With this point as a center, draw an arc tangent to the belt line. Lines tangent to this arc will determine diameters of other pulleys requiring the same belt length.

When crossed belts are used, the sum of the diameters of each pair of pulleys must be equal to the sum of the diameters of every other pair.

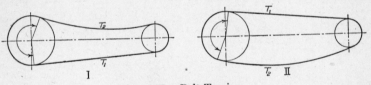

FIG. 173. Belt Tension.

132. Horsepower Transmitted by Belts.—Power is transmitted by a belt because one side is tighter than the other. The difference in pull on the two sides depends upon the tightness of the belt, the friction between the belt and the pulley and the arc of contact or wrap of the belt around the pulley. The tight side of a belt should come on the bottom so that any sagging of the belt will increase the arc of contact as at I, Fig. 173, where T_1 is the tension in the tight side and T_2 in the slack side.

The power transmitted by a belt is determined by the difference in tensions and the speed of the belt. The horsepower transmitted is equal to the effective pull times the speed divided by 33,000 which may be written as a formula.

$$\frac{(T_1 - T_2)V}{33,000} = \text{HP},$$

T_1 = Tension on tight side in lbs.,
T_2 = Tension on slack side in lbs.,
V = Speed in feet per minute.

The value of T_1 may be taken at 35 to 50 lbs. per inch of width for single belts and 60 to 90 lbs. per inch of width for double belts. The value of V should be less than 2,000 feet per minute when this formula is used.

For higher speeds the effect of centrifugal force must be considered. (See Machinery's Handbook or Mark's Handbook.)

Common empirical rules often used are:

$$1 \text{ HP} = \frac{WV}{1000} \text{ for single belts}$$

and

$$1 \text{ HP} = \frac{WV}{600} \text{ for double belts.}$$

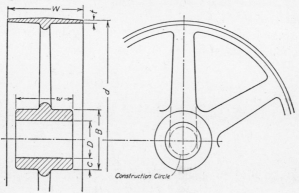

FIG. 174. Pulley Proportions.

133. Pulley Proportions.—Some proportions of cast iron pulleys are shown in Fig. 174. Note the construction circle for the pulley arms.

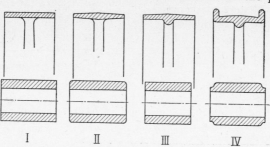

FIG. 175. Rims and Hubs.

The taper toward the rim may be $\frac{1}{4}''$ to $\frac{3}{8}''$ per foot on each side. In the left hand view the taper may be about half as much. Several forms of rims and hubs are indicated in Fig. 175. In order to prevent a belt from slipping off, the face of the pulley may be provided with flanges as at

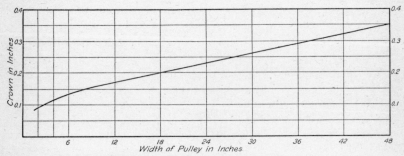

FIG. 176. Crowning Chart.

IV, Fig. 175. The usual method, however, is to use a "crowned" pulley as at II and III. The belt tends to "ride" on the highest part of the pulley. The amount of crowning varies greatly but may be taken from Fig. 176.

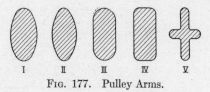

FIG. 177. Pulley Arms.

134. Pulley arms are commonly made elliptical in section although

TABLE 16

STANDARD KEYSEAT DIMENSIONS
For Pulleys and Rope Sheaves

Diameter of Shaft, Inches	W	T	Diameter of Shaft, Inches	W	T
$^{15}/_{16}$—$1^{1}/_{8}$	$^{1}/_{4}$	$^{1}/_{8}$	$3^{7}/_{16}$—$3^{5}/_{8}$	$^{7}/_{8}$	$^{7}/_{16}$
$1^{3}/_{16}$—$1^{3}/_{8}$	$^{5}/_{16}$	$^{5}/_{32}$	$3^{11}/_{16}$—$3^{7}/_{8}$	$^{15}/_{16}$	$^{15}/_{32}$
$1^{7}/_{16}$—$1^{5}/_{8}$	$^{3}/_{8}$	$^{3}/_{16}$	$3^{15}/_{16}$—$4^{1}/_{8}$	1	$^{1}/_{2}$
$1^{11}/_{16}$—$1^{7}/_{8}$	$^{7}/_{16}$	$^{7}/_{32}$	$4^{3}/_{16}$—$4^{5}/_{8}$	$1^{1}/_{8}$	$^{1}/_{2}$
$1^{15}/_{16}$—$2^{1}/_{8}$	$^{1}/_{2}$	$^{1}/_{4}$	$4^{11}/_{16}$—$5^{3}/_{8}$	$1^{1}/_{4}$	$^{1}/_{2}$
$2^{3}/_{16}$—$2^{3}/_{8}$	$^{9}/_{16}$	$^{9}/_{32}$	$5^{7}/_{16}$—$5^{5}/_{8}$	$1^{3}/_{8}$	$^{1}/_{2}$
$2^{7}/_{16}$—$2^{5}/_{8}$	$^{5}/_{8}$	$^{5}/_{16}$	$5^{11}/_{16}$—$6^{7}/_{8}$	$1^{1}/_{2}$	$^{5}/_{8}$
$2^{11}/_{16}$—$2^{7}/_{8}$	$^{11}/_{16}$	$^{11}/_{32}$	$6^{15}/_{16}$—$7^{7}/_{8}$	$1^{3}/_{4}$	$^{3}/_{4}$
$2^{15}/_{16}$—$3^{1}/_{8}$	$^{3}/_{4}$	$^{3}/_{8}$	$7^{15}/_{16}$—$8^{7}/_{8}$	2	$^{3}/_{4}$
$3^{3}/_{16}$—$3^{3}/_{8}$	$^{13}/_{16}$	$^{13}/_{32}$			

FIG. 178. Keyseats.

other sections are sometimes used, Fig. 177. Standard keyseat dimensions for pulley hubs are given with Fig. 178 in Table 16.

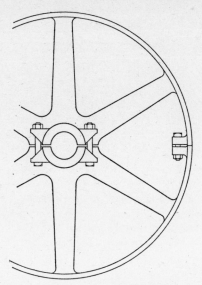

FIG. 179. C. I. Split Pulley.

135. For convenience, cast iron split pulleys, Fig. 179, are made. Steel pulleys are light and strong and can be used at higher speeds than cast iron. For some purposes wood pulleys, Fig. 180, are desirable.

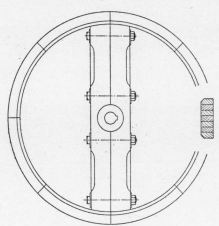

FIG. 180. Wood Pulley.

CHAPTER VII

SHAFTING AND COUPLINGS

136. Shafting.—Shafting is made from various grades of wrought iron and steel. Cold rolled shafting is much used. This is shafting which has been cleaned of scale and rolled under pressure. It can be used for many purposes without machining to size and is considerably strengthened by the surface which comes from the rolling process. Cold rolled shafting is ordinarily made in diameters starting at $3/16''$, increasing by $1/16''$ and in lengths up to 24 feet.

Hot rolled shafting is "black" and must be turned to size before using. Actual diameters are $1/16''$ less than nominal diameters.

137. Standard Sizes.—It is probable that diameters of shafting will be standardized in order to do away with the present great variety. Desirable sizes for standard shafting are reported in the A. S. M. E. Journal (Mechanical Engineering, April, 1920) as follows:

Transmission Shafting Diameters:
$15/16''$; $1 3/16''$; $1 7/16''$; $1 11/16''$; $1 15/16''$; $2 3/16''$; $2 7/16''$; $2 15/16''$; $3 7/16''$; $3 15/16''$; $4 7/16''$; $4 15/16''$; $5 7/16''$; $5 15/16''$.

Machinery Shafting Diameters:
Size intervals extending to $2 1/2$ in., by sixteenth inches; from $2 1/2$ in., to 4 in., inclusive by eighth inches; and from 4 in., to 6 in., by quarter inches.

138. Special Shafts.—Special shafts have to be forged of steel suitable for the particular purpose. Shafts for machine tools and power machinery are made with varying diameters and must be completely dimensioned as indicated in Fig. 126.

139. To Compute the Diameter of a Shaft.—The diameter of a shaft for a given purpose will depend upon the material, the speed, and the character of the load. If a force is applied at a distance from the center of a shaft it will tend to twist the shaft, Fig. 181. The measure of this

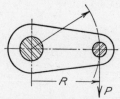

Fig. 181.

twisting tendency is called the twisting moment and is equal to $M_t = PR$ in which P = pounds and R = inches. The moment of the stress within the shaft must equal this twisting moment, or

$$M_t = PR = \frac{S'J}{r},$$

in which S' = shearing stress in pounds per square inch, r = radius of shaft in inches, and J = polar moment of inertia.

For a solid shaft $J = \pi d^4/32$ in which d = diameter of shaft.

Then $PR = S'\pi d^3/16$ or solving the equation for d this becomes

$$d = \frac{\sqrt[3]{16PR}}{\pi S'},$$

which is the formula for figuring the size of a solid shaft.

For a hollow shaft

$$PR = \frac{S'\pi(d_1^4 - d_2^4)}{16d_1},$$

in which d_1 = outside diameter and d_2 = inside diameter.

140. Horse Power Transmitted.—To figure a shaft for a given horse power let H.P. = horsepower = 33,000 ft. lbs. per minute and N = number of revolutions per minute.

$$\text{H.P.} = \frac{PR2\pi N}{12 \times 33,000}.$$

Substitute the value $S'\pi d^3/16$ for PR and the equation may be put into the form

$$d = \frac{\sqrt[3]{321,000 \text{ H.P.}}}{S'N}.$$

This formula may be written

$$d = k \frac{\sqrt[3]{\text{HP}}}{N}.$$

Values of k for different values of S' are given in Table 17.

TABLE 17

S'	k	S'	k
3,000........	4.75	7,000.........	3.57
4,000........	4.31	8,000.........	3.42
5,000........	4.00	9,000.........	3.29
6,000........	3.77		

For main shafts S' may be taken at 3,000 to 4,000. For line shafts with pulleys etc., use $S' = 5,000$. For counter shafts and other short shafts the value of S' may be from 7,000 to 9,000.

141. The formula $d = k \sqrt[3]{(\text{H.P.}/N)}$ may be solved for the horsepower and written in the form

$$\text{H.P.} = \frac{d^3 N}{\text{Constant}}.$$

TABLE 18

VALUES OF d^3N

Dia. of Shaft in In.	Revolutions per Minute							
	100	125	150	175	200	250	300	350
	d^3N	d^3N	d^3N	d^3N	d^3N	d^3N	d^3N	d^3N
$1/2$	12.50	15.66	18.75	21.88	25.00	31.32	37.50	43.76
$5/8$	24.41	30.51	36.62	42.72	48.82	61.02	73.23	85.44
$3/4$	42.19	52.74	63.30	73.83	84.38	105.5	126.6	147.6
$7/8$	66.99	83.74	100.5	117.3	134.0	167.1	201.0	234.0
1	100.0	125.0	150.0	175.0	200.0	250.0	300.0	350.0
$1^1/8$	142.4	178.0	213.6	249.2	284.8	356.0	427.2	498.4
$1^1/4$	195.3	244.1	293.0	341.8	390.6	488.2	585.9	683.6
$1^3/8$	260.0	325.0	390.0	455.0	520.0	650.0	780.0	910.0
$1^1/2$	337.5	421.9	506.3	590.6	675.0	843.8	1013.	1181.
$1^5/8$	429.1	536.4	643.7	750.9	858.2	1073.	1287.	1501.
$1^{11}/16$	480.6	600.8	720.9	841.0	961.2	1202.	1442.	1682.
$1^{15}/16$	727.3	909.1	1091.	1273.	1455.	1818.	2182.	2546.
$2^3/16$	1047.	1309.	1571.	1832.	2094.	2618.	3141.	3664.
$2^1/4$	1139.	1424.	1709.	1993.	2278.	2848.	3417.	3986.
$2^5/16$	1237.	1546.	1856.	2165.	2474.	3092.	3711.	4330.
$2^7/16$	1448.	1810.	2172.	2534.	2896.	3620.	4344.	5068.
$2^{11}/16$	1941.	2426.	2912.	3397.	3882.	4852.	5823.	6794.
$2^{15}/16$	2535.	3169.	3803.	4436.	5070.	6338.	7605.	8872.
$3^7/16$	4062.	5078.	6093.	7110.	8124.	10160.	12190.	14200.
$3^{15}/16$	6105.	7631.	9158.	10680.	12210.	15260.	18320.	21360.
$4^1/2$	9113.	11390.	13670.	15950.	18226.	22780.	27340.	31900.
5	12500.	15630.	18750.	21880.	25000.	31260.	37500.	43760.
$5^1/2$	16640.	20800.	24960.	29120.	33280.	41600.	49910.	58240.
6	21600.	27000.	32400.	37800.	43200.	54000.	64800.	75600.

Values of this constant as given by the B. F. Sturtevant Co., follow.

Turned steel shafting, head shafts, well supported. Constant = 125.
Cold rolled shafting, head shafts, well supported. Constant = 100.
Turned steel shafting, line shafts, bearings 8 ft. apart. Constant = 90.
Cold rolled shafting, line shafts, bearings 8 ft. apart. Constant = 70.
Turned steel shafting, countershafts, bearings not over 8 ft. apart. Constant = 50.
Cold rolled shafting, countershafts bearings not over 8 ft. apart. Constant = 40.

Values of d^3N are given in Table 18.

142. Shaft for Bending and Twisting.—When a shaft carries a heavy flywheel or is otherwise subject to bending as well as twisting we must allow for both stresses. This is done by finding a moment equivalent to the bending and twisting moments together using the formula

$$M_e = M + \sqrt{M_t{}^2 + M^2}.$$

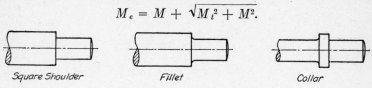

Square Shoulder   Fillet   Collar

Fig. 182.   Square and Filleted Shoulders.

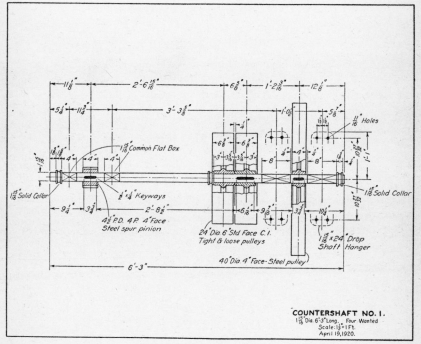

Fig. 183.   A Shafting Drawing.

in which M_e = equivalent moment. M = bending moment and M_t = twisting moment.

The formula for diameter then is

$$d = \frac{\sqrt[3]{16M_e}}{\pi S'}.$$

143. Shaft Details.—Methods of dimensioning shafts and other details are given in Chap. IV. Square and filleted shoulders and a shaft collar are indicated in Fig. 182. The filleted form is of course, stronger than the square corner shoulder. A part of a shafting drawing is shown in Fig. 183. Note the various series of dimensions, the location of bearings, pulleys and other details.

144. Couplings.—Couplings for joining lengths of shafting together are made in many forms. A solid sleeve or box coupling is a hollow cylinder which holds the ends of the shafts, Fig. 184. Set screws or keys are used to hold the shafts in place. Table 19 gives dimensions.*

TABLE 19 (Fig. 184)

* Dimensions of Solid Sleeve Couplings

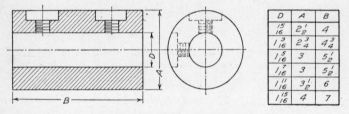

D	A	B
$\frac{15}{16}$	$2\frac{1}{2}$	4
$1\frac{3}{16}$	$2\frac{3}{4}$	$4\frac{3}{4}$
$1\frac{5}{16}$	3	$5\frac{1}{2}$
$1\frac{7}{16}$	3	$5\frac{1}{2}$
$1\frac{11}{16}$	$3\frac{1}{2}$	6
$1\frac{15}{16}$	4	7

Fig. 184. Solid Sleeve Coupling.

145. The split box or clamp coupling shown in Fig. 185, is made in halves which are bolted together and are keyed to the two shafts. Some dimensions are given in Table 20.

146. A simple flange coupling is illustrated in Fig. 186. Each half is keyed to the end of a shaft and the two halves bolted together. Some dimensions are given in Table 21.

* Tables 19 to 22 are from the Royersford Foundry and Machine Company, Inc.

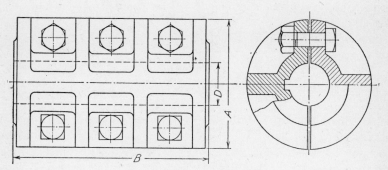

FIG. 185. Clamp Coupling.

TABLE 20 (FIG. 185)

* DIMENSIONS OF CLAMP COUPLINGS

Size of Shaft, Inches	A	B	Size of Keyseat	Bolts	
				No.	Size
$^{15}/_{16}$ and 1	$5^3/_8$	4	$^1/_4$	4	$^1/_2$
$1^3/_{16}$ and $1^1/_4$	$6^1/_4$	$4^1/_4$	$^1/_4$	4	$^1/_2$
$1^7/_{16}$ and $1^1/_2$	$7^1/_8$	$4^1/_2$	$^3/_8$	6	$^1/_2$
$1^{11}/_{16}$ and $1^3/_4$	$8^1/_4$	$5^1/_8$	$^7/_{16}$	6	$^5/_8$
$1^{15}/_{16}$ and 2	$8^5/_8$	$5^1/_2$	$^1/_2$	6	$^5/_8$
$2^3/_{16}$ and $2^1/_4$	$9^5/_{16}$	$5^3/_4$	$^9/_{16}$	6	$^3/_4$
$2^7/_{16}$ and $2^1/_2$	$9^7/_8$	$6^1/_4$	$^5/_8$	6	$^3/_4$
$2^{11}/_{16}$ and $2^3/_4$	$10^7/_8$	$7^1/_4$	$^{11}/_{16}$	6	$^3/_4$
$2^{15}/_{16}$ and 3	12	$7^1/_4$	$^3/_4$	6	$^7/_8$
$3^3/_{16}$ and $3^1/_4$	$12^7/_8$	$7^7/_8$	$^3/_4$	6	$^7/_8$
$3^7/_{16}$ and $3^1/_2$	$13^1/_2$	8	$^7/_8$	6	$^7/_8$
$3^{11}/_{16}$ and $3^3/_4$	$14^1/_4$	$9^1/_2$	$^7/_8$	6	$^7/_8$
$3^{15}/_{16}$ and 4	$15^1/_2$	$10^1/_4$	1	6	1
$4^3/_{16}$ and $4^1/_4$	$17^1/_2$	$10^1/_2$	1	8	1
$4^7/_{16}$ and $4^1/_2$	$17^1/_2$	11	$1^1/_8$	8	1
$4^{11}/_{16}$ and $4^3/_4$	$18^3/_8$	11	$1^1/_8$	8	1
$4^{15}/_{16}$ and 5	$18^3/_8$	$11^3/_4$	$1^1/_4$	8	$1^1/_8$
$5^3/_{16}$ and $5^1/_4$	$19^1/_4$	$14^1/_4$	$1^1/_4$	8	$1^1/_4$
$5^7/_{16}$ and $5^1/_2$	$19^1/_4$	$14^1/_4$	$1^3/_8$	8	$1^1/_4$
$5^{11}/_{16}$ and $5^3/_4$	20	16	$1^3/_8$	8	$1^3/_8$
$5^{15}/_{16}$ and 6	20	16	$1^1/_2$	8	$1^3/_8$
$6^7/_{16}$ and $6^1/_2$	$22^3/_8$	....	$1^5/_8$	....	....
$6^{15}/_{16}$ and 7	$23^1/_4$	....	$1^3/_4$	....	....

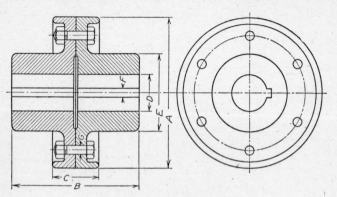

Fig. 186.　Flange Coupling.

TABLE 21 (Fig. 186)

* Flange Couplings

Size of Shaft, Inches	A	B	C	D	Size of Keyway	Bolts	
						No.	Size
$^{15}/_{16}$ and 1	$4^7/_8$	$3^1/_4$	$1^5/_8$	$1^7/_8$	$^1/_4$	3	$^1/_2$
$1^3/_{16}$ and $1^1/_4$	$6^3/_4$	$4^7/_8$	$2^1/_8$	$2^3/_4$	$^5/_{16}$	4	$^1/_2$
$1^7/_{16}$ and $1^1/_2$	$7^5/_8$	$5^5/_8$	$2^3/_8$	$3^3/_8$	$^3/_8$	5	$^1/_2$
$1^{11}/_{16}$ and $1^3/_4$	$8^3/_8$	$6^1/_2$	$2^1/_2$	4	$^7/_{16}$	5	$^5/_8$
$1^{15}/_{16}$ and 2	9	$7^3/_8$	$2^7/_8$	$4^1/_2$	$^1/_2$	5	$^5/_8$
$2^3/_{16}$ and $2^1/_4$	$9^1/_2$	$8^1/_4$	3	5	$^9/_{16}$	5	$^5/_8$
$2^7/_{16}$ and $2^1/_2$	$10^1/_4$	9	$3^1/_4$	$5^1/_4$	$^5/_8$	6	$^5/_8$
$2^{11}/_{16}$ and $2^3/_4$	$10^3/_4$	10	$3^1/_4$	$6^1/_4$	$^{11}/_{16}$	6	$^3/_4$
$2^{15}/_{16}$ and 3	$10^7/_8$	10	$3^1/_4$	$6^1/_4$	$^3/_4$	6	$^3/_4$
$3^3/_{16}$ and $3^1/_4$	12	$10^7/_8$	$3^3/_8$	$6^3/_4$	$^3/_4$	6	$^3/_4$
$3^7/_{16}$ and $3^1/_2$	$12^1/_4$	$10^7/_8$	$3^3/_8$	$6^3/_4$	$^7/_8$	6	$^3/_4$
$3^{11}/_{16}$ and $3^3/_4$	13	$11^1/_8$	$3^7/_8$	$6^7/_8$	$^7/_8$	6	$^3/_4$
$3^{15}/_{16}$ and 4	13	$11^1/_8$	$3^7/_8$	8	1	6	$^3/_4$
$4^3/_{16}$ and $4^1/_4$	$14^3/_8$	$11^3/_8$	4	8	1	6	$^7/_8$
$4^7/_{16}$ and $4^1/_2$	$14^3/_8$	$11^3/_8$	$4^1/_8$	$8^1/_2$	$1^1/_8$	6	$^7/_8$
$4^{11}/_{16}$ and $4^3/_4$	$16^1/_2$	$13^7/_8$	$5^3/_4$	$10^1/_2$	$1^1/_8$	8	$^7/_8$
$4^{15}/_{16}$ and 5	$16^1/_2$	$13^7/_8$	$5^3/_4$	$10^1/_2$	$1^1/_4$	8	$^7/_8$
$5^3/_{16}$ and $5^1/_4$	$17^3/_4$	$14^3/_4$	6	$10^1/_2$	$1^1/_4$	8	$^7/_8$
$5^7/_{16}$ and $5^1/_2$	$17^3/_4$	$14^3/_4$	6	$10^3/_4$	$1^3/_8$	8	$^7/_8$
$5^{11}/_{16}$ and $5^3/_4$	19	16	$6^1/_2$	11	$1^3/_8$	6	1
$5^{15}/_{16}$ and 6	19	16	$6^1/_2$	$11^1/_4$	$1^1/_2$	6	1

A square jaw clutch coupling is shown in Fig. 187 and dimensions are given in Table 22.

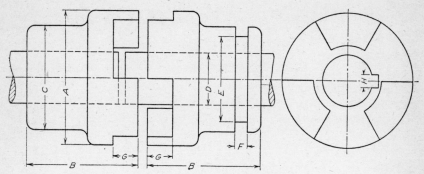

FIG. 187. Square Jaw Coupling.

TABLE 22 (FIG. 187)

* JAW CLUTCH COUPLINGS

Size of Shaft, Inches	A	B	C	E	F	G	Size of Keyway
$^{15}/_{16}$ and 1	....	....	....	....	.....	.....	$^{5}/_{16}$
$1^{3}/_{16}$ and $1^{1}/_{4}$	$3^{7}/_{8}$	$3^{7}/_{8}$	3	$2^{7}/_{16}$	$^{7}/_{8}$	$^{7}/_{16}$	$^{5}/_{16}$
$1^{7}/_{16}$ and $1^{1}/_{2}$	$3^{7}/_{8}$	$3^{7}/_{8}$	3	$2^{7}/_{16}$	$^{7}/_{8}$	$^{7}/_{16}$	$^{3}/_{8}$
$1^{11}/_{16}$ and $1^{3}/_{4}$	$4^{1}/_{4}$	$4^{1}/_{4}$	$3^{3}/_{4}$	$2^{3}/_{4}$	$^{15}/_{16}$	$^{1}/_{2}$	$^{7}/_{16}$
$1^{15}/_{16}$ and 2	$4^{7}/_{16}$	$5^{1}/_{8}$	4	$3^{1}/_{4}$	1	$^{1}/_{2}$	$^{1}/_{2}$
$2^{3}/_{16}$ and $2^{1}/_{4}$	$4^{1}/_{2}$	$5^{1}/_{2}$	$4^{1}/_{4}$	$3^{1}/_{4}$	$^{15}/_{16}$	$^{9}/_{16}$	$^{9}/_{16}$
$2^{7}/_{16}$ and $2^{1}/_{2}$	$4^{3}/_{4}$	6.	$4^{5}/_{8}$	$3^{5}/_{8}$	1	$^{5}/_{8}$	$^{5}/_{8}$
$2^{11}/_{16}$ and $2^{3}/_{4}$	5	$6^{1}/_{2}$	$4^{3}/_{4}$	4	1	$^{5}/_{8}$	$^{11}/_{16}$
$2^{15}/_{16}$ and 3	$5^{1}/_{8}$	7	$5^{1}/_{4}$	$4^{15}/_{16}$	1	$^{5}/_{8}$	$^{3}/_{4}$
$3^{3}/_{16}$ and $3^{1}/_{4}$	$5^{1}/_{4}$	$7^{5}/_{8}$	$5^{1}/_{2}$	$4^{3}/_{4}$	$1^{1}/_{16}$	$^{5}/_{8}$	$^{7}/_{8}$
$3^{7}/_{16}$ and $3^{1}/_{2}$	$5^{5}/_{8}$	$8^{1}/_{4}$	$6^{1}/_{8}$	5	$1^{1}/_{16}$	$^{3}/_{4}$	$^{7}/_{8}$
$3^{11}/_{16}$ and $3^{3}/_{4}$	....	....	....	....	.....	.....	....
$3^{15}/_{16}$ and 4	7	$9^{1}/_{2}$	7	$5^{1}/_{2}$	$1^{1}/_{8}$	$^{3}/_{4}$	1
$4^{7}/_{16}$ and $4^{1}/_{2}$	7	11	8	$6^{1}/_{2}$	$1^{1}/_{8}$	$^{3}/_{4}$	$1^{1}/_{8}$
$4^{15}/_{16}$ and 5	.....	....	....	....	.....	.....	....
$5^{7}/_{16}$ and $5^{1}/_{2}$	....	....	....	....	.....	.....	....
$5^{15}/_{16}$ and 6	....	....	....	....	.....	.....	....
$6^{7}/_{16}$ and $6^{1}/_{2}$	....	....	....	....	.....	.....	....
$6^{15}/_{16}$ and 7	....	....	....	....	.....	.....	....

CHAPTER VIII

JIGS, FIXTURES, AND DETAILS

147. Jigs and Fixtures.—It is not the purpose of this book to discuss the design of jigs and fixtures but a few suggestions bearing upon the drafting of such devices will be given.

Jigs and fixtures have come into existence through the standardizing of operations necessary for quantity production and interchangeable manufacture.

148. Fixtures.—The terms, jigs and fixtures are often used for the same thing. A fixture may be considered as a device to hold work on a machine in the proper position for the different operations and is dependent upon the action of the machine to accomplish its purpose. Fixtures are classified by the machines with which they are used and the method of machining, operating, etc. A milling machine fixture might be considered as typical.

149. Jigs.—A jig may be considered as a device for holding a piece to insure uniformity when a number are to be made. For instance a drilling jig would hold a piece and provide a means for guiding the drill so that each piece would have the holes drilled alike. It is not dependent upon the machine with which it is used. Jigs might be classed as cast iron box jigs, template type, interchangeable bushing type, etc.

150. Jig and Fixture Drawings.—The general procedure for making drawings of shop devices is similar to any other kind of design drawing.

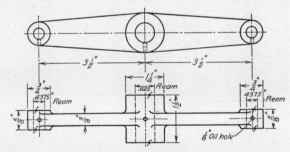

Fig. 188. Simple Beam Detail.

The "production," or part to be machined should be drawn first, using light pencil lines or other distinctive representation, to show its

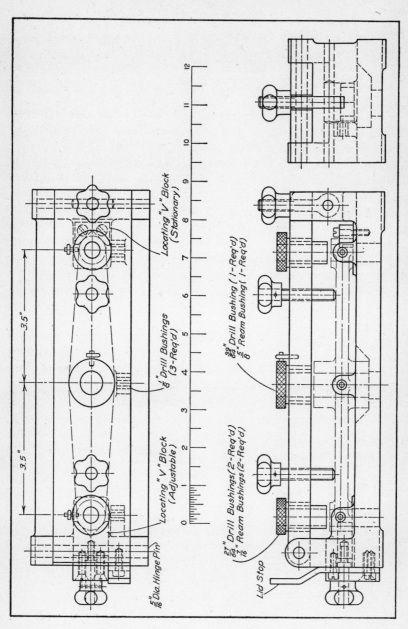

FIG. 189. Jig for Drilling and Reaming Simple Beam.

form after the operations have been completed.   The jig or fixture can then be designed "around" the piece.

The considerations given in Art. 153 should be kept in mind.   Finished surfaces should be indicated and necessary dimensions given.   Limits of accuracy must be specified where required.

151. A typical jig drawing for the *simple beam* of Fig. 188 is shown in position in Fig. 189.   The *work* is shown in position by light dash lines. The work rests upon the finished pads of the *body* and is held by the two screws which pass through the *lid*.   Two "*V*" *blocks*, one of which is adjustable, fix the work in its horizontal position.   The bushings for drilling and reaming are held in the lid.   The lid is hinged at the left end and clamped at the right end.

152. A fixture drawing for the *arm detail* of Fig. 190 is shown in Fig. 191.   Two swinging blocks are used to locate the arm for the first

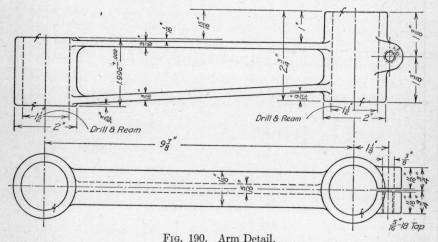

Fig. 190.   Arm Detail.

operation.   These are then dropped down and two large blocks are used to hold the end which has been machined while the second operation is performed.   Figs. 188 to 191 are from drawings kindly supplied by Arthur Brock, Jr., Tool and Manufacturing Works.

153. Fixture Design.—The many forms of jigs and fixtures will not be described here and the reader is referred to the books and articles on this subject.

The Cincinnati Milling Machine Company in their "Treatise on Milling and Milling Machines"* have a chapter on jigs and fixtures which

* Published by Cincinnati Milling Machine Co., Cincinnati, O.   Price $1.50.

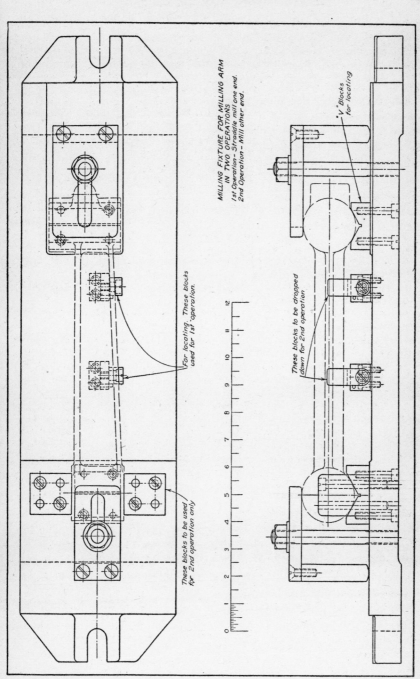

MILLING FIXTURE FOR MILLING ARM
IN TWO OPERATIONS
1st Operation - Straddle mill one end.
2nd Operation - Mill other end.

"V" Blocks
for locating

For locating These blocks
used for 1st operation.

These blocks to be dropped
down for 2nd operation

These blocks to be used
for 2nd operation only

FIG. 191. Fixture for Milling Arm.

has been used in the preparation of these articles including the following, "Axioms for the Fixture Designer."

1. The clamp should be immediately above the supporting point.

> NOTE.—Disregard of this leads to springing of the work, or lifting of the work due to support point being transformed into a fulcrum.

2. Three fixed supporting points should be the maximum for any rough surfaces.

3. Supporting points for finished surfaces should be as small in area as is consistent with the pressure to be exerted by the clamps.

4. All supporting points should be set as far apart as the nature of the work will allow.

5. All side clamps should be arranged to press downward.

6. The fixed supporting points should always circumscribe the center of gravity of the work.

7. All supporting points over and above the original three should be sensitive in their adjustment.

8. All clamps and adjusting supports should be operated from the front of the fixture.

9. All clamps and support points that are operated or locked by wrench should have the same size head.

10. Support points should be set so high above the body of the fixture as to minimize the amount of cleaning required.

11. Support points should have provision for easy removing and replacing in the event of breakage.

12. Fixed support points should have provision for adjustments to take care of variations in castings from time to time.

13. Clamps should be arranged so that they can be easily withdrawn from the work.

> NOTE.—This is to avoid lengthy unscrewing of the nut in order to give ample clearance between clamp and work.

14. Springs should be used to hold clamp up against clamping nut.

> NOTE.—This is to avoid the falling down of the clamp and the consequent loss of time attendant on holding it up while inserting the work beneath.

15. Supporting points and clamps to be accessible to the operator's hand and eye.

16. Adequate provision for taking up end thrust so that this will not be dependent upon friction between work and clamp.

All of the above axioms are applicable to almost every type of fixture.

154. Some considerations in the design of fixtures are given as:

"1. Rapidity of Clamping.

"2. Accessibility for Inserting and Removing work.

"3. Generous Ducts for the Escape of Chips and Lubricant.

"4. Removal of the Clamping and Supporting Members from the Cutter Zone.   (Safety of Operation.)

"5. Elimination of Clamping Strains from Table of Machine and Absorption of Same in Fixture.

"6. Provision of Mass in Excess of Necessary Rigidity to absorb Chatter."

155. Standard Parts for Jigs and Fixtures.—There are certain standard constructions and parts of jigs and fixtures with which the designer must become familiar, especially those used in his own line of work.

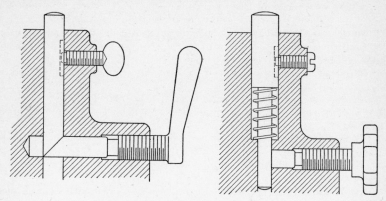

FIG. 192. Adjustable Support Pins.

Such details as bushings, handles, clamping devices, support pins, setting pieces, etc., might be considered. A few parts are given in Figs.

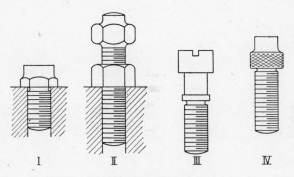

I   II   III   IV

FIG. 193. Support Pins and Screws.

192 to 194, to which the reader should add sketches of special devices and arrangements. Dimensions will be found in the various machine handbooks. Table 23 of standardized bushings is condensed from the data sheet book of the Wright-Fisher Bushing Corporation, who publish very complete tables of dimensions of their standardized bushings, liners etc. Diameters may be had varying by $1/64''$ and in four standard lengths for each size.

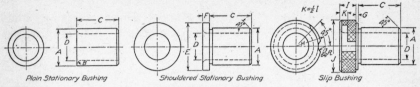

Fᴵɢ. 194. Bushings.

TABLE 23 (Fɪɢ. 194)

Dɪᴍᴇɴꜱɪᴏɴꜱ ᴏꜰ Sᴛᴀɴᴅᴀʀᴅɪᴢᴇᴅ Bᴜꜱʜɪɴɢꜱ

D	A	B	C	E	F	G	H	I	J
$1/8$	$5/16$	$1/32$	$3/8$	$7/16$	$1/16$	$1/16$	$1/2$	$1/4$	$11/16$
$3/16$	$3/8$	$1/32$	$3/8$	$1/2$	$3/32$	$1/16$	$17/32$	$1/4$	$3/4$
$1/4$	$7/16$	$1/32$	$3/8$	$9/16$	$3/32$	$1/16$	$19/32$	$1/4$	$7/8$
$5/16$	$9/16$	$1/32$	$7/16$	$11/16$	$3/32$	$1/16$	$21/32$	$7/16$	1
$3/8$	$5/8$	$1/16$	$1/2$	$3/4$	$3/32$	$1/16$	$11/16$	$7/16$	$1\,1/16$
$7/16$	$11/16$	$1/16$	$9/16$	$13/16$	$1/8$	$1/16$	$23/32$	$7/16$	$1\,1/8$
$1/2$	$3/4$	$3/32$	$9/16$	$7/8$	$1/8$	$1/16$	$25/32$	$1/2$	$1\,1/4$
$9/16$	$13/16$	$3/32$	$5/8$	1	$1/8$	$1/16$	$13/16$	$1/2$	$1\,5/16$
$5/8$	$7/8$	$3/32$	$3/4$	$1\,1/8$	$3/16$	$1/16$	$7/8$	$1/2$	$1\,7/16$
$11/16$	1	$1/8$	$7/8$	$1\,1/4$	$3/16$	$3/32$	$15/16$	$1/2$	$1\,9/16$
$3/4$	$1\,1/16$	$1/8$	$1\,1/8$	$1\,5/16$	$3/16$	$3/32$	$31/32$	$1/2$	$1\,5/8$
$13/16$	$1\,1/8$	$1/8$	$1\,1/4$	$1\,3/8$	$3/16$	$3/32$	1	$1/2$	$1\,11/16$
$7/8$	$1\,1/4$	$1/8$	$1\,3/8$	$1\,9/16$	$1/4$	$3/32$	$1\,1/16$	$1/2$	$1\,13/16$
$15/16$	$1\,5/16$	$1/8$	$1\,1/2$	$1\,11/16$	$1/4$	$3/32$	$1\,3/32$	$1/2$	$1\,7/8$
1	$1\,3/8$	$5/32$	$1\,5/8$	$1\,3/4$	$1/4$	$3/32$	$1\,1/8$	$5/8$	$1\,15/16$

156. Standard Parts and Details.—When making drawings of machinery it is always desirable and often absolutely necessary to consider the shop facilities available. This means that the designer should know the machines which will be used for making the parts and how they will be used.

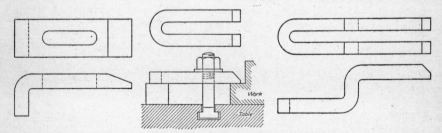

Fɪɢ. 195. Common Clamps.

Some of the smaller appliances used about the shop should be familiar to the draftsman. Some usual clamps are shown in Fig. 195. If standard equipment is on hand this is a simple matter that can often be used to advantage when deciding on how to hold a machine part for finishing.

157. The application of holding devices is shown in Fig. 196, and drawings for some "CAD" standardized appliances are shown in Fig.

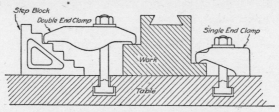

FIG. 196. Holding Devices Applied.

197. Drawings and dimensions were furnished by Mr. H. Cadawallader, Jr., of the Standard Shop Equipment Co., Philadelphia, Pa. Such de-

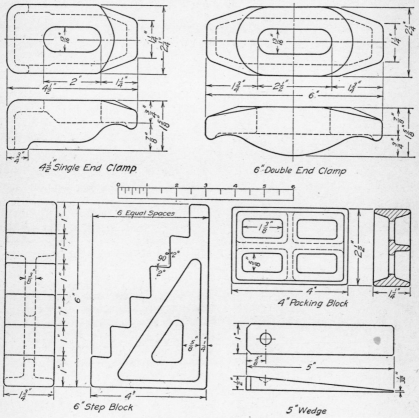

FIG. 197. Standardized Appliances.

vices can be purchased ready for use in a great variety of sizes and forms and save a great deal of time.

158. The tables and notes which follow will suggest further information which the draftsman should have available in handbooks and note

FIG. 198. A Lathe Mandrel.

books. Standard T slots are given in Table 24, and "CAD" steel washers and machine table bolts in Tables 25 and 26. Standard tapers such as Jarno, Brown and Sharpe, Morse, etc., are given in full in the American Machinist and Machinery Handbooks. A lathe mandrel is drawn in Fig. 198 and a pipe tap in Fig. 199.

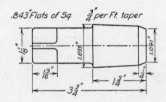

FIG. 199. Pipe Tap.

TABLE 24

DIMENSIONS OF STANDARD "T" SLOTS

A....	1/4	5/16	3/8	7/16	1/2	5/8	3/4	7/8	1
B....	1/2	5/8	11/16	13/16	15/16	1 3/16	1	1 1/16	1 3/16
C....	5/32	5/32	7/32	7/32	9/32	13/32	17/32	11/16	13/16
D....	5/16	3/8	7/16	7/16	9/16	3/4	1	1 1/16	1 3/16

TABLE 25

DIMENSIONS OF STEEL WASHERS

Bolt Dia..	3/8	1/2	5/8	3/4
A........	13/32	17/32	21/32	25/32
B........	7/8	1	1 1/4	1 1/2
C........	1/8	3/16	1/4	1/4

TABLE 26

DIMENSIONS OF MACHINE TABLE BOLTS

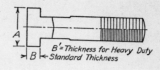

B' = Thickness for Heavy Duty
B ← Standard Thickness

Bolt Dia...	$3/8$	$1/2$	$5/8$	$3/4$	$7/8$	1
A....	$5/8$	$7/8$	$1\,1/16$	$1\,3/16$	$1\,1/2$	$1\,3/4$
B....	$5/32$	$1/4$	$5/16$	$7/16$	$9/16$	$5/8$
B'....	$1/4$	$11/32$	$15/32$	$9/16$	....	

CHAPTER IX

GEARS AND CAMS

159. This chapter is intended to give an introductory knowledge of gears and cams so that drawings of them can be made and understood.

For a complete theoretical treatment a good text on mechanism or a special book on gears or cams should be studied.

160. Pulleys and Gears.—Consider two discs or wheels secured on shafts and placed so that the surfaces of the wheels are in contact, Fig. 200. If one of the wheels is turned and there is no slipping, the other

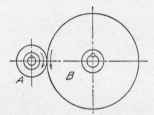

Fig. 200. Friction Wheels.

will turn, but in an opposite direction. If the pulley A has a diameter of $3''$ and the pulley B a diameter of $9''$, it will be necessary for pulley A to make three revolutions while pulley B makes one revolution. The velocity ratio is 3.

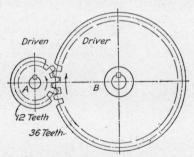

Fig. 201. Pinion and Gear.

If the forces are large or it is necessary to prevent slipping, gear teeth may be added to the two wheels as in Fig. 201. The ratio of velocities

114

or the number of turns for gears is figured by using the number of teeth on each wheel. In the figure gear A has 14 teeth and gear B has 49 teeth, so that gear A must make $49/14 = 3^1/_2$ turns for one turn of gear B. The smaller of the two gears is called a pinion.

The direction of revolution is indicated. The diameters, or number of teeth, or revolutions may be calculated by the formulas which follow:

T_1 = number of teeth in first gear
N_1 = revolutions per minute of first gear
D_1 = diameter of first gear
R_1 = radius of first gear
T_2 = number of teeth in second gear
N_2 = revolutions per minute of second gear
D_2 = diameter of second gear
R_2 = radius of second gear.

Then

$$\frac{T_1}{T_2} = \frac{N_2}{N_1}, \qquad \frac{D_1}{D_2} = \frac{N_2}{N_1}, \qquad \frac{R_1}{R_2} = \frac{N_2}{N_1}.$$

It is not always convenient to have the wheels in contact and other considerations often make it necessary to separate the pulleys or wheels.

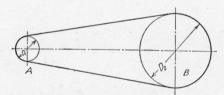

FIG. 202. Belt Drive.

Some form of belt, rope or chain is then used as in Fig. 202. The formulas for Figs. 200 and 202 are:—

$$\frac{D_1}{D_2} = \frac{N_2}{N_1}, \qquad \frac{R_1}{R_2} = \frac{N_2}{N_1}.$$

161. Gear Teeth.—Some of the terms used in gear work and the names of parts of gear teeth are illustrated and named in Fig. 203. The pitch circles are circles having diameters of rolling cylinders which would have the same velocity ratio as the gears which replace them.

The circular pitch as illustrated is the distance from a point on one tooth to the same point on the next tooth measured along the pitch circle.

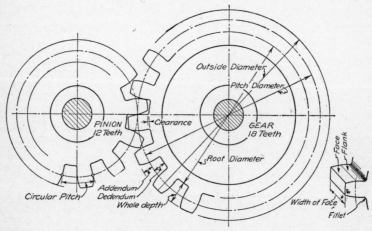

F IG . 203. Gear Terms.

The diametral pitch is the number of teeth per inch of pitch diameter. The other terms can be understood from the illustration.

162. Spur Gears.—The gear wheels just described are called spur gears. The tooth outline for gears may be either a cycloid or an involute. The cycloidal system is used for large cast gears. For most purposes cut gears are now used. These are made on the involute system. The calculations for spur gears may be made from the formulas which follow.

P = diametral pitch,

P_c = circular pitch,

N = number of teeth,

D_p = pitch diameter,

D_o = outside diameter,

$\dfrac{1}{P}$ = addendum,

$\dfrac{1 + .157}{P}$ = dedendum,

$\dfrac{2 + .157}{P}$ = depth of cut.

$P = \dfrac{\pi}{P_c}$	$D_p = \dfrac{N}{P}$	$N = D_p \times P$
$P = \dfrac{N}{D_p}$	$D_p = D_0 - \dfrac{2}{P}$	$N = PD_0 - 2$
$P_c = \dfrac{\pi}{P}$	$D_0 = \dfrac{N+2}{P}$	$N = \dfrac{\pi D_p}{P_c}$
$P_c = \dfrac{\pi D_p}{N}$	$D_0 = D_p + \dfrac{2}{P}$	

163. Spur Gear Drawing.—It is not necessary to draw the tooth outline for cut gears. The gear specifications required for cut gears are outside diameter, diametral pitch, depth of cut, and number of teeth. A spur gear drawing with dimensions is shown in Fig. 204. Note that

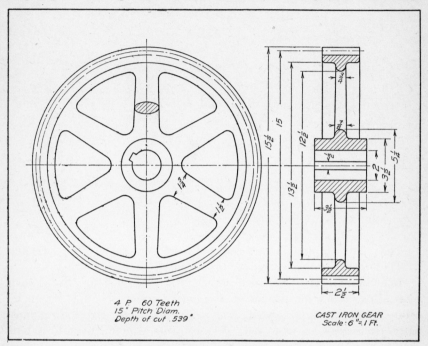

4 P 60 Teeth
15" Pitch Diam.
Depth of cut .539"

CAST IRON GEAR
Scale : 6"= 1 Ft.

FIG. 204. A Spur Gear Drawing.

the teeth are not shown and are not sectioned. Root diameter is represented by a dash line, the pitch diameter by a dot and dash line, and the outside diameter by a full line. Hubs, arms and rims are discussed in Chap. VI.

164. Bevel Gears.—Two cones in contact might be used to transmit

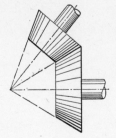

FIG. 205. Friction Cones.

motion from one shaft to another as in Fig. 205. To prevent slipping, teeth may be used and the cones become bevel gears. Two bevel gears

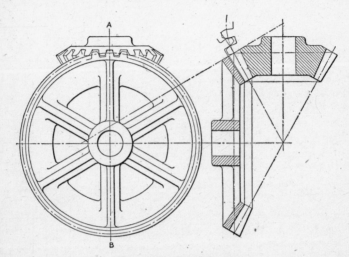

FIG. 206. Bevel Gears.

of the same size with shafts at right angles are called mitre gears. A pair of bevel gears is shown in Fig. 206. The shafts may make any angle with each other. The terms used and the parts of a bevel gear are given

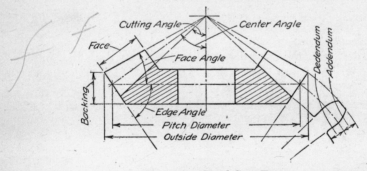

FIG. 207. Bevel Gear Terms.

in Fig. 207. Note the location of the pitch diameter and that the addendum and dedendum are measured at the large end of the gear tooth. A bevel gear drawing is shown in Fig. 208.

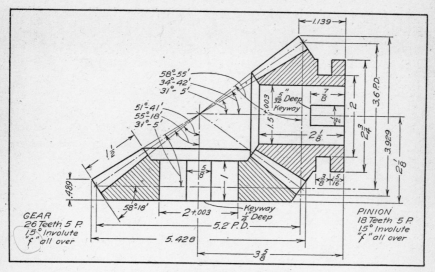

FIG. 208. Bevel Gear Drawing.

165. Worm Gearing.—A worm and wheel are shown in Fig. 209. A worm is a screw having a section on a plane through its axis of the same form as an involute rack tooth. The gear which is driven by the worm

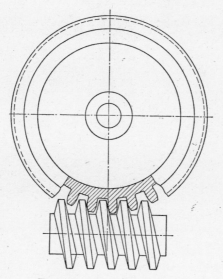

FIG. 209. Worm and Wheel.

is called a worm wheel. The worm may have single, double, or multiple threads as explained in Chapter II for screw threads. The velocity ratio is found by dividing the number of teeth in the worm wheel by 1 for a single thread worm, by 2 for a double thread worm, etc. A worm and wheel drawing are given in Fig. 210.

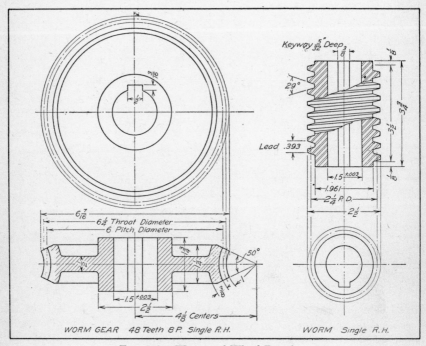

FIG. 210. Worm and Wheel Drawing.

166. Cams.—A cam is a plate having a curved outline or groove, or a cylinder having a groove, and is used to change rotary motion to re-

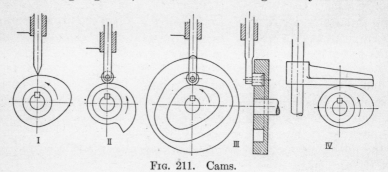

FIG. 211. Cams.

ciprocating motion. The reciprocating motion may be variable or intermittent. The part to which motion is given is called the follower. Several forms of cams are shown in Fig. 211.

167. To Draw a Plate Cam.—A cam outline is required which will raise the follower with uniform motion a distance of $1\frac{1}{2}''$ during one third of a revolution of the cam.

The follower is dropped uniformly during the next third of a revolution and remains at rest for one third of a revolution. Refer to Fig. 212.

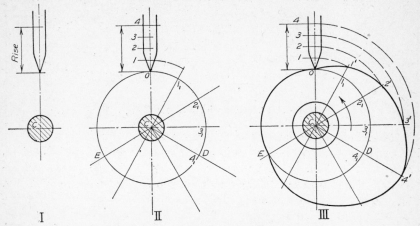

FIG. 212. Cam with Point Follower.

Given the center of the cam, C and the rise of the follower, $O4$. With C as a center and radius CO, draw a circle. Divide this circle into three equal parts by radii CD, and CE. Then divide rise into a number of equal parts as shown at 1, 2, 3 and 4. Divide arc OD into same number of equal parts and draw radii through points thus located as at II. With C as a center and radius $C1$ draw arc cutting radius $C1_1$, produced at $1'$ as shown at III. Then $C2' = C2$; $C3' = C3$; $C4' = C4$. A smooth curve through points $1'$, $2'$, $3'$, and $4'$ will give a part of the cam outline. The curve from $4'$ to E is found by laying off the true distances on each radius as for the rise. Since the follower is to be at rest an arc from E to O with radius CO will complete the cam outline.

168. If a roller is used instead of a point on the follower the cam will be smaller. Proceed as for Fig. 212 which will give the curve followed by the center of the roll shown in Fig. 213 as a dot and dash line and called the pitch line. With a radius equal to the radius of the roll and centers on the pitch line draw arcs to which a tangent curve can be drawn to give the cam outline.

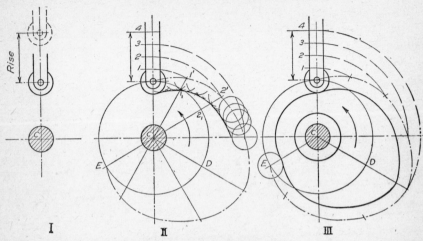

FIG. 213.   Cam with Roller Follower.

169. Kinds of Motion.—The follower may have *uniform motion* as in the cases described,—*harmonic motion, uniformly accelerated motion,* or *irregular motion.* If the follower rises equal distances in equal intervals of time, we have uniform motion, shown in a diagram at I, Fig. 214. When uniform motion is used, a circular arc is often used at the

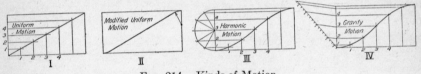

FIG. 214.   Kinds of Motion.

beginning and end to decrease the shock of sudden starting and stopping, Fig. 214 at II.

170. The diagram for harmonic motion is shown at III. Points on the travel of the follower are located by drawing a semi-circle, dividing it into a number of equal parts and drawing lines to the line of travel as shown. A cam with this motion can be run at a higher speed. The unequal distances vertically on the line of travel are moved over in equal intervals of time.

171. Uniformly accelerated motion gives the easiest working cam. The follower has the same motion as a falling body. The distance passed over is proportional to the square of the time. The distances on the travel of the follower are made proportional to 1, 3, 5, 7, etc., and reverse as shown at IV, Fig. 214.

Other kinds of motion are used to meet special conditions.

172. When the center of the follower is not in line with the vertical radius, Fig. 215. The follower is to rise uniformly during one half revolu-

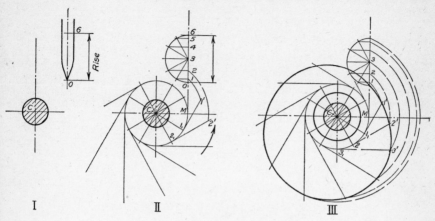

FIG. 215. Cam with Offset Follower.

tion and fall during the second half. Draw center line of follower down until it crosses horizontal center line through cam at M. With CM as a radius draw a circle. Divide rise of follower in parts to give harmonic motion. Divide one half of the circle just drawn into as many equal parts as there are spaces in the rise, and draw tangents at each point as shown. With C as a center draw an arc passing through point 1 on the rise and cutting tangent from point 1_1 at $1'$. Arcs with C as a center and passing through points 2, 3, and 4 will locate other points through which a smooth curve can be passed.

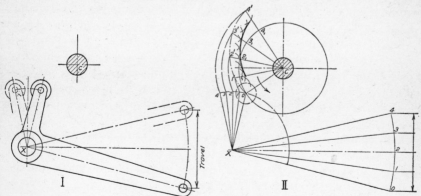

FIG. 216. Cam with Lever Follower.

173. When levers are used to transmit motion from the cam, Fig. 216, the method of solution is similar to the previous cases.   Given the center of the cam shaft, center of bell crank shaft, lengths of arms and travel required at end of long arm as shown at I.

The end of the long arm is to rise uniformly during one third revolution, drop half way down instantly, remain at rest one third revolution and drop uniformly during the remaining third of a revolution.

Draw arcs with X as a center.   Divide the travel into a number of equal parts and draw horizontal lines to locate points on the large arc. Find corresponding points on the small arc.   The points on the cam outline are then located as shown in the figure.

174. The construction for a cam with flat follower is shown in Fig. **217.**   The follower is to rise during one half revolution, remain at rest

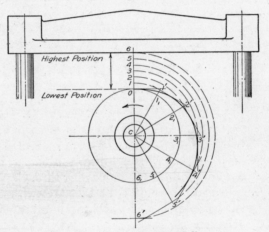

Fig. 217.   Cam with Flat Follower.

one sixth of a revolution and fall during the remaining one third revolution.   Divide the rise into a number of equal parts.   Draw circle with CO as a radius.   Divide arc CD into same number of equal parts as rise.   Draw radial lines.   Lay off distances $C1$, $C2$, etc., on the radii to locate points 1, 2, etc., at points $1'$, $2'$, etc., draw perpendiculars to the radii.   A smooth curve drawn tangent to these perpendiculars will be the cam outline.

175. Cylindrical Cams.—A cylindrical cam is a cylinder having a groove which gives the desired motion to a roller, Fig. 218.   The pitch line for a cylindrical cam is first drawn on the development of the cam surface.   Fig. 219 illustrates the solution of a cylindrical cam problem.

The travel is indicated on the figure. The follower is to move one half the distance with uniform motion during one fourth of a revolution,

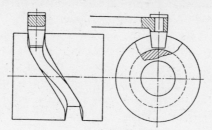

FIG. 218. Cylindrical Cam.

remain at rest one fourth of a revolution, rise uniformly during one fourth revolution and drop with harmonic motion during the remaining one fourth revolution. Divide the circle into a number of equal parts and lay them off on the stretchout line. The first three quarters of a revolu-

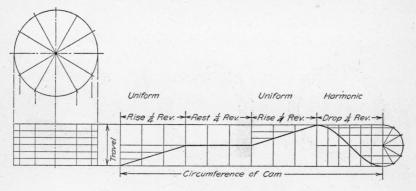

FIG. 219. Cylindrical Cam Development.

tion are evident in the figure. The last quarter has as many equal horizontal divisions as there are unequal or harmonic divisions in the travel.

For a complete treatment of the subject of cams consult Professor Furman's "Cams—Elementary and Advanced," Wiley, N. Y.

CHAPTER X

PIPING DRAWINGS

176. Piping.—The frequent occurance of piping in engineering work makes it necessary for the machine draftsman to know something about the sizes of pipe, fittings, etc., and their representation. For a complete treatment see the author's "Handbook on Piping," D. Van Nostrand Co., N. Y. The following material is based upon the above book.

177. Uses and Materials.—Piping is used for conveying fluids—steam, gas, air, water, etc., and is made of cast iron, wrought iron, steel, lead, brass and other materials. Cast iron pipe is cheaply made and is used for underground gas, water, and drain pipes, sometimes for exhaust steam and for low pressure steam. Wrought pipe, of iron or steel, is most commonly used, especially for high pressures. For hot or impure water, brass pipe is preferred as it does not corrode like iron or steel. Spiral riveted piping is often used for large diameters.

Standard   Extra Heavy   Double Extra Heavy

FIG. 220. Sections of $\frac{3}{4}''$ Pipe.

178. Pipe Sizes.—Wrought pipe is specified by its nominal inside diameter for sizes up to 12 inches. The Brigg's Standard dimensions are used in America. The nominal diameter varies from actual diameter as indicated in the dimensions, Table 27. Standard pipe is used for pressures up to 125 pounds per square inch. Extra strong and double extra strong pipe are made for use at high pressures. The extra thickness is obtained by reducing the inside diameter, the outside remaining constant for a given nominal diameter, Tables 28 and 29. Actual cross sections for the three weights of $\frac{3}{4}''$ pipe are shown in Fig. 220. Above twelve inches, pipe is known as *O.D.* or outside diameter pipe and is specified accordingly. The thickness may be any desired amount.

179. Pipe Fittings, Valves, etc.—For joining lengths of pipe and

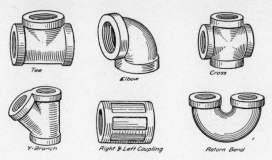

Tee

Elbow

Cross

Y-Branch

Right & Left Coupling

Return Bend

FIG. 221. Screwed Pipe Fittings.

making turns and connections, fittings are used, Fig. 221. Such fittings consist of flanges, couplings, tees, ells, crosses, etc. Small pipe is "made up" by means of screwed fittings, Fig. 222. Some dimensions are given in Table 30. A screwed union and a flanged union are shown in Fig. 223.

180. Flanged Fittings.—Flanged Fittings, Fig. 227 are to be preferred for important or high pressure work. Regular fittings are now

TABLE 27

STANDARD PIPE THREADS

Size Inches	Threads per Inch	Diameter of Tap Drill Inches	Outside Diameter of Threads at End of Pipe Inches	Depth of Threads Inches	Number of Perfect Threads	Length of Perfect Threads Inches
$1/8$	27	$21/64$	.393	.029	5.13	.19
$1/4$	18	$27/64$	.522	.044	5.22	.29
$3/8$	18	$9/16$	.656	.044	5.4	.30
$1/2$	14	$11/16$	.815	.057	5.46	.39
$3/4$	14	$29/32$	1.025	.057	5.6	.40
1	$11 1/2$	$1 1/8$	1.283	.069	5.87	.51
$1 1/4$	$11 1/2$	$1 15/32$	1.626	.069	6.21	.54
$1 1/2$	$11 1/2$	$1 23/32$	1.866	.069	6.33	.55
2	$11 1/2$	$2 3/16$	2.339	.069	6.67	.58
$2 1/2$	8	$2 9/16$	2.819	.100	7.12	.89
3	8	$3 3/16$	3.441	.100	7.6	.95
$3 1/2$	8	$3 11/16$	3.938	.100	8.0	1.00
4	8	$4 3/16$	4.434	.100	8.4	1.05
$4 1/2$	8	$4 3/4$	4.931	.100	8.8	1.10
5	8	$5 5/16$	5.490	.100	9.28	1.16
6	8	$6 5/16$	6.546	.100	10.08	1.26
7	8	....	7.540	.100	10.88	1.36
8	8	....	8.534	.100	11.68	1.46
9	8	....	9.527	.100	12.56	1.57
10	8	....	10.645	.100	13.44	1.68

TABLE 28
Extra Strong Wrought Pipe

Nominal Size	External Diameter Inches	Internal Diameter Inches	Thickness Inches	Weight per Foot Plain Ends Pounds	Internal Area Sq. Inches	Length of Pipe per Square Foot of	
						External Surface Feet	Internal Surface Feet
1/8	.405	.215	.095	.314	.036	9.431	17.766
1/4	.540	.302	.119	.535	.072	7.073	12.648
3/8	.675	.423	.126	.738	.141	5.658	9.030
1/2	.840	.546	.147	1.087	.234	4.547	6.995
3/4	1.050	.742	.154	1.473	.433	3.637	5.147
1	1.315	.957	.179	2.171	.719	2.904	3.991
1 1/4	1.660	1.278	.191	2.996	1.283	2.301	2.988
1 1/2	1.900	1.500	.200	3.631	1.767	2.010	2.546
2	2.375	1.939	.218	5.022	2.953	1.608	1.969
2 1/2	2.875	2.323	.276	7.661	4.238	1.328	1.644
3	3.500	2.900	.300	10.252	6.605	1.091	1.317
3 1/2	4.000	3.364	.318	12.505	8.888	.954	1.135
4	4.500	3.826	.337	14.983	11.497	.848	.998
4 1/2	5.000	4.290	.355	17.611	14.455	.763	.890
5	5.563	4.813	.375	20.778	18.194	.686	.793
6	6.625	5.761	.432	28.573	26.067	.576	.663
7	7.625	6.625	.500	38.048	34.472	.500	.576
8	8.625	7.625	.500	43.388	45.663	.442	.500
9	9.625	8.625	.500	48.728	58.426	.396	.442
10	10.750	9.750	.500	54.735	74.662	.355	.391
11	11.750	10.750	.500	60.075	90.763	.325	.355
12	12.750	11.750	.500	65.415	108.434	.299	.325

TABLE 29
Double Extra Strong Wrought Pipe

Nominal Size	External Diameter Inches	Approximate Internal Diameter Inches	Thickness Inches	Weight per Foot Plain Ends Pounds	Internal Area Sq. Inches	Length of Pipe per Square Foot of	
						External Surface Feet	Internal Surface Feet
1/2	.840	.252	.294	1.714	.050	4.547	15.157
3/4	1.050	.434	.308	2.440	.148	3.637	8.801
1	1.315	.599	.358	3.659	.282	2.904	6.376
1 1/4	1.660	.896	.382	5.214	.630	2.301	4.263
1 1/2	1.900	1.100	.400	6.408	.950	2.010	3.472
2	2.375	1.503	.436	9.029	1.774	1.608	2.541
2 1/2	2.875	1.771	.552	13.695	2.464	1.328	2.156
3	3.500	2.300	.600	18.583	4.155	1.091	1.660
3 1/2	4.000	2.728	.636	22.850	5.845	.954	1.400
4	4.500	3.152	.674	27.541	7.803	.848	1.211
4 1/2	5.000	3.580	.710	32.530	10.066	.763	1.066
5	5.563	4.063	.750	38.552	12.966	.686	.940
6	6.625	4.897	.864	53.160	18.835	.576	.780
7	7.625	5.875	.875	63.079	27.109	.500	.650
8	8.625	6.875	.875	72.424	37.122	.442	.555

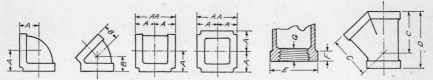

FIG. 222.   Walworth C. 1. Fittings.

TABLE 30

WALWORTH CO., STANDARD CAST IRON FITTINGS

Size of Pipe, Inches	A Inches	A–A Inches	B Inches	C Inches	D Inches	E Inches	F Inches	G Inches
$1/4$	$3/4$	$1^1/2$	$7/16$	. . . .	. . . .	1	$1/4$	$3/8$
$3/8$	$7/8$	$1^3/4$	$9/16$	$1^7/16$	$2^1/16$	$1^1/8$	$5/16$	$7/16$
$1/2$	$1^1/16$	$2^1/8$	$11/16$	$1^7/8$	$2^9/16$	$1^7/16$	$3/8$	$1/2$
$3/4$	$1^5/16$	$2^5/8$	$13/16$	$2^1/16$	$2^3/4$	$1^3/4$	$7/16$	$9/16$
1	$1^1/2$	3	$15/16$	$2^1/2$	$3^1/4$	$2^1/16$	$1/2$	$5/8$
$1^1/4$	$1^{13}/16$	$3^5/8$	$1^1/16$	3	$3^3/4$	$2^1/2$	$9/16$	$11/16$
$1^1/2$	2	4	$1^3/16$	$3^1/4$	$4^3/4$	$2^3/4$	$5/8$	$13/16$
2	$2^3/8$	$4^3/4$	$1^3/8$	4	$5^1/2$	$3^3/8$	$11/16$	$7/8$
$2^1/2$	$2^7/8$	$5^3/4$	$1^5/8$	5	$6^{13}/16$	$4^1/8$	$13/16$	1
3	$3^5/16$	$6^5/8$	$1^7/8$	$5^5/8$	$7^5/8$	$4^3/4$	$15/16$	1
$3^1/2$	$3^{11}/16$	$7^3/8$	$2^1/16$	$6^3/8$	$8^3/4$	$5^1/4$	1	$1^1/16$
4	4	8	$2^1/4$	$7^1/8$	$9^3/4$	6	$1^1/16$	$1^1/8$
$4^1/2$	$4^7/16$	$8^7/8$	$2^7/16$	$7^7/8$	$10^1/2$	$6^9/16$	$1^1/8$	$1^1/4$
5	$4^{11}/16$	$9^3/8$	$2^9/16$	$8^1/2$	$11^5/16$	$7^1/16$	$1^1/8$	$1^1/4$
6	$5^5/16$	$10^5/8$	$2^{13}/16$	$9^{15}/16$	$13^1/8$	$8^3/8$	$1^1/8$	$1^3/8$
7	$6^1/16$	$12^1/8$	$3^1/8$	$11^1/4$	$14^5/8$	$9^3/4$	$1^3/16$	$1^1/2$
8	$6^{13}/16$	$13^5/8$	$3^9/16$	$12^{15}/16$	$16^{13}/16$	$10^7/8$	$1^3/8$	$1^5/8$
9	$7^1/2$	15	$3^7/8$	$14^1/2$	19	$12^1/8$	$1^7/16$	$1^3/4$
10	$8^1/4$	$16^1/2$	$4^5/16$	16	$20^7/8$	$13^1/4$	$1^5/8$	$1^3/4$
12	$9^9/16$	$19^1/8$	$4^7/8$	. . . .	. . . .	$15^5/8$	$1^3/4$	$1^7/8$

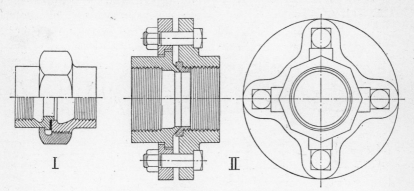

I   II

FIG. 223.   Screwed Union and Flanged Union.

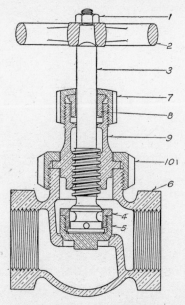

FIG. 224.   Globe Valve.

made with dimensions of the American Standard as devised by a committee of the A. S. M. E., and a Manufacturers' committee.   This
standard fixes the dimensions for standard weight fittings (125 lbs.)
from 1 inch to 100 inches and for extra heavy or high pressure fittings
(250 lbs.) from 1 inch to 48 inches.   The following tables give some of
the dimensions, revised to March 7th and 20th, 1914.

181. Valves.—There are two general classes of valves, globe valves
and gate valves.   The globe valve has a spherical body and a circular
opening at right angles to the axis of the pipe.   A section of a globe
valve, together with the names of the principal parts is shown in Fig. 224.

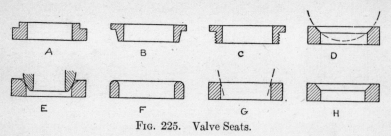

FIG. 225.   Valve Seats.

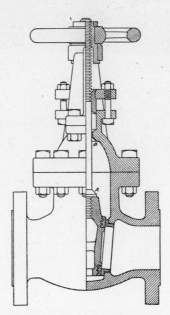

FIG. 226.   Gate Valve.

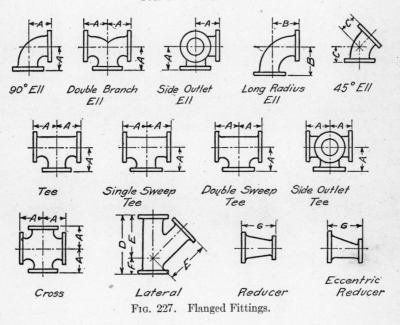

FIG. 227.   Flanged Fittings.

Names of Parts of Globe Valve

1. Stem nut,
2. Hand wheel,
3. Valve stem,
4. Valve nut,
5. Valve (swivel),

6. Valve body,
7. Gland nut,
8. Gland,
9. Bonnet,
10. Bonnet ring.

A valve may be used in place of an elbow and a globe valve, in which case it is called an angle valve. There are several objections to the use of globe valves, among which are the resistance which they offer to the fluid and the water pocket which is present when they are used for steam lines. They are desirable, however, when throttling is necessary.

TABLE 31 (Fig. 227)

American Standard Flanged Fittings

125 Pounds Working Pressure

Size Inches	A–A Inches	A Inches	B Inches	C Inches	D Inches	E Inches	F Inches	G Inches
1	7	$3^1/_2$	5	$1^3/_4$	$7^1/_2$	$5^3/_4$	$1^3/_4$	....
$1^1/_4$	$7^1/_2$	$3^3/_4$	$5^1/_2$	2	8	$6^1/_4$	$1^3/_4$	....
$1^1/_2$	8	4	6	$2^1/_4$	9	7	2	....
2	9	$4^1/_2$	$6^1/_2$	$2^1/_2$	$10^1/_2$	8	$2^1/_2$	....
$2^1/_2$	10	5	7	3	12	$9^1/_2$	$2^1/_2$	....
3	11	$5^1/_2$	$7^3/_4$	3	13	10	3	6
$3^1/_2$	12	6	$8^1/_2$	$3^1/_2$	$14^1/_2$	$11^1/_2$	3	$6^1/_2$
4	13	$6^1/_2$	9	4	15	12	3	7
$4^1/_2$	14	7	$9^1/_2$	4	$15^1/_2$	$12^1/_2$	3	$7^1/_2$
5	15	$7^1/_2$	$10^1/_4$	$4^1/_2$	17	$13^1/_2$	$3^1/_2$	8
6	16	8	$11^1/_2$	5	18	$14^1/_2$	$3^1/_2$	9
7	17	$8^1/_2$	$12^3/_4$	$5^1/_2$	$20^1/_2$	$16^1/_2$	4	10
8	18	9	14	$5^1/_2$	22	$17^1/_2$	$4^1/_2$	11
9	20	10	$15^1/_4$	6	24	$19^1/_2$	$4^1/_2$	$11^1/_2$
10	22	11	$16^1/_2$	$6^1/_2$	$25^1/_2$	$20^1/_2$	5	12
12	24	12	19	$7^1/_2$	30	$24^1/_2$	$5^1/_2$	14
14	28	14	$21^1/_2$	$7^1/_2$	33	27	6	16
15	29	$14^1/_2$	$22^3/_4$	8	$34^1/_2$	$28^1/_2$	6	17
16	30	15	24	8	$36^1/_2$	30	$6^1/_2$	18
18	33	$16^1/_2$	$26^1/_2$	$8^1/_2$	39	32	7	19
20	36	18	29	$9^1/_2$	43	35	8	20
22	40	20	$31^1/_2$	10	46	$37^1/_2$	$8^1/_2$	22
24	44	22	34	11	$49^1/_2$	$40^1/_2$	9	24
26	46	23	$36^1/_2$	13	53	44	9	26
28	48	24	39	14	56	$46^1/_2$	$9^1/_2$	28
30	50	25	$41^1/_2$	15	59	49	10	30
32	52	26	44	16	....	....	....	32
34	54	27	$46^1/_2$	17	....	....	....	34
36	56	28	49	18	....	....	....	36
38	58	29	$51^1/_2$	19	....	....	....	38
40	60	30	54	20	....	....	....	40

A variety of valve seats is shown in Fig. 225. In the figure A, B and C are plain flat seats; D is a concave or spherical seat; E and F are rounded seats; G is a square seat and H is a bevel seat. Any of these forms may be made as a part of the valve body or separate, and either screwed or forced into place.

A gate valve is shown in section in Fig. 226, and as will be observed has its openings parallel to the cross section of the pipe, so there is little or no resistance to the flow, making it preferable for most purposes.

TABLE 32 (Fig. 227)

EXTRA HEAVY AMERICAN STANDARD FLANGED FITTINGS

250 Pounds Working Pressure

Size Inches	A–A Inches	A Inches	B Inches	C Inches	D Inches	E Inches	F Inches	G Inches
1	8	4	5	2	$8^1/_2$	$6^1/_2$	2	. . . .
$1^1/_4$	$8^1/_2$	$4^1/_4$	$5^1/_2$	$2^1/_2$	$9^1/_2$	$7^1/_4$	$2^1/_4$	. . . .
$1^1/_2$	9	$4^1/_2$	6	$2^3/_4$	11	$8^1/_2$	$2^1/_2$	. . . .
2	10	5	$6^1/_2$	3	$11^1/_2$	9	$2^1/_2$	. . . .
$2^1/_2$	11	$5^1/_2$	7	$3^1/_2$	13	$10^1/_2$	$2^1/_2$	. . . .
3	12	6	$7^3/_4$	$3^1/_2$	14	11	3	6
$3^1/_2$	13	$6^1/_2$	$8^1/_2$	4	$15^1/_2$	$12^1/_2$	3	$6^1/_2$
4	14	7	9	$4^1/_2$	$16^1/_2$	$13^1/_2$	3	7
$4^1/_2$	15	$7^1/_2$	$9^1/_2$	$4^1/_2$	18	$14^1/_2$	$3^1/_2$	$7^1/_2$
5	16	8	$10^1/_4$	5	$18^1/_2$	15	$3^1/_2$	8
6	17	$8^1/_2$	$11^1/_2$	$5^1/_2$	$21^1/_2$	$17^1/_2$	4	9
7	18	9	$12^3/_4$	6	$23^1/_2$	19	$4^1/_2$	10
8	20	10	14	6	$25^1/_2$	$20^1/_2$	5	11
9	21	$10^1/_2$	$15^1/_4$	$6^1/_2$	$27^1/_2$	$22^1/_2$	5	$11^1/_2$
10	23	$11^1/_2$	$16^1/_2$	7	$29^1/_2$	24	$5^1/_2$	12
12	26	13	19	8	$33^1/_2$	$27^1/_2$	6	14
14	30	15	$21^1/_2$	$8^1/_2$	$37^1/_2$	31	$6^1/_2$	16
15	31	$15^1/_2$	$22^3/_4$	9	$39^1/_2$	33	$6^1/_2$	17
16	33	$16^1/_2$	24	$9^1/_2$	42	$34^1/_2$	$7^1/_2$	18
18	36	18	$26^1/_2$	10	$45^1/_2$	$37^1/_2$	8	19
20	39	$19^1/_2$	29	$10^1/_2$	49	$40^1/_2$	$8^1/_2$	20
22	41	$20^1/_2$	$31^1/_2$	11	53	$43^1/_2$	$9^1/_2$	22
24	45	$22^1/_2$	34	12	$57^1/_2$	$47^1/_2$	10	24
26	48	24	$36^1/_2$	13	. . . .	. . . .	. . . .	26
28	52	26	39	14	. . . .	. . . .	. . . .	28
30	55	$27^1/_2$	$41^1/_2$	15	. . . .	. . . .	. . . .	30
32	58	29	44	16	. . . .	. . . .	. . . .	32
34	61	$30^1/_2$	$46^1/_2$	17	. . . .	. . . .	. . . .	34
36	65	$32^1/_2$	49	18	. . . .	. . . .	. . . .	36
38	68	34	$51^1/_2$	19	. . . .	. . . .	. . . .	38
40	71	$35^1/_2$	54	20	. . . .	. . . .	. . . .	40
42	74	37	$56^1/_2$	21	. . . .	. . . .	. . . . . .	42
44	78	39	59	22	. . . .	. . . .	. . . . . .	44
46	81	$40^1/_2$	$61^1/_2$	23	. . . .	. . . .	. . . . . .	46
48	84	42	64	24	. . . .	. . . .	. . . .	48

TABLE 33

AMERICAN STANDARD PIPE FLANGES

125 Pounds Working Pressure

Size Inches	Diameter of Flanges Inches	Thickness of Flanges Inches	Bolt Circle Inches	Number of Bolts	Size of Bolts Inches	Length of Bolts Inches	Length of Studs with Two Nuts Inches
1	4	$7/16$	3	4	$7/16$	$1^1/2$	....
$1^1/4$	$4^1/2$	$1/2$	$3^3/8$	4	$7/16$	$1^1/2$	....
$1^1/2$	5	$9/16$	$3^7/8$	4	$1/2$	$1^3/4$	....
2	6	$5/8$	$4^3/4$	4	$5/8$	2	....
$2^1/2$	7	$11/16$	$5^1/2$	4	$5/8$	$2^1/4$	....
3	$7^1/2$	$3/4$	6	4	$5/8$	$2^1/2$	....
$3^1/2$	$8^1/2$	$13/16$	7	4	$5/8$	$2^1/2$	....
4	9	$15/16$	$7^1/2$	8	$5/8$	$2^3/4$	....
$4^1/2$	$9^1/4$	$15/16$	$7^3/4$	8	$3/4$	3	....
5	10	$15/16$	$8^1/2$	8	$3/4$	3	....
6	11	1	$9^1/2$	8	$3/4$	3	....
7	$12^1/2$	$1^1/16$	$10^3/4$	8	$3/4$	3	....
8	$13^1/2$	$1^1/8$	$11^3/4$	8	$3/4$	$3^1/4$	....
9	15	$1^1/8$	$13^1/4$	12	$3/4$	$3^1/4$	....
10	16	$1^3/16$	$14^1/4$	12	$7/8$	$3^1/2$	....
12	19	$1^1/4$	17	12	$7/8$	$3^3/4$	....
14	21	$1^3/8$	$18^3/4$	12	1	$4^1/4$	....
15	$22^1/4$	$1^3/8$	20	16	1	$4^1/4$	....
16	$23^1/2$	$1^7/16$	$21^1/4$	16	1	$4^1/4$	....
18	25	$1^9/16$	$22^3/4$	16	$1^1/8$	$4^3/4$	....
20	$27^1/2$	$1^{11}/16$	25	20	$1^1/8$	5	....
22	$29^1/2$	$1^{13}/16$	$27^1/4$	20	$1^1/4$	$5^1/2$	....
24	32	$1^7/8$	$29^1/2$	20	$1^1/4$	$5^1/2$	....
26	$34^1/4$	2	$31^3/4$	24	$1^1/4$	$5^3/4$	....
28	$36^1/2$	$2^1/16$	34	28	$1^1/4$	6	....
30	$38^3/4$	$2^1/8$	36	28	$1^3/8$	$6^1/4$	....
32	$41^3/4$	$2^1/4$	$38^1/2$	28	$1^1/2$	$6^1/2$	....
34	$43^3/4$	$2^5/16$	$40^1/2$	32	$1^1/2$	$6^1/2$	....
36	46	$2^3/8$	$42^3/4$	32	$1^1/2$	7	....
38	$48^3/4$	$2^3/8$	$45^1/4$	32	$1^5/8$	7	9
40	$50^3/4$	$2^1/2$	$47^1/4$	36	$1^5/8$	7	9

When drawn to a small scale, valves and fittings are shown by conventional representations such as Figs. 228 and 229. Apparatus used in connection with piping as well as the machines to which it is connected, is frequently represented by diagrams such as Fig. 230, where the numbers correspond to the following list.

1, 2. Plan of Direct Acting Steam Pump.

3, 4, 5. Elevation of Direct Acting Steam Pump.

6. End View of Direct Acting Steam Pump.

7, 8, 9. Separator.

10, 11. Receiver—or Receiver Separator.

12. Vertical Steam Engine.

13. Plan of Horizontal Steam Engine.

14, 15. Steam Trap.

16. Feed Water Heater.

17. End View Horizontal Steam Engine.

18. Plan of Water Tube Boiler.

19. Elevation of Water Tube Boiler.

20. Plan of Fire Tube Boiler.

21. Centrifugal Pump.

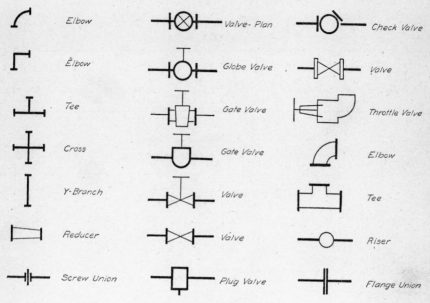

Fig. 228. Single Line Conventions.

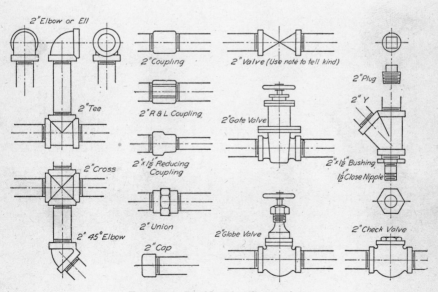

Fig. 229. Double Line Conventions.

TABLE 34

EXTRA HEAVY AMERICAN STANDARD PIPE FLANGES

250 Pounds Working Pressure

Size Inches	Diameter of Flanges Inches	Thickness of Flanges Inches	Bolt Circle Inches	Number of Bolts	Size of Bolts Inches	Length of Bolts Inches	Length of Studs with Two Nuts Inches
1	$4^1/_2$	$^{11}/_{16}$	$3^1/_4$	4	$^1/_2$	2	....
$1^1/_4$	5	$^3/_4$	$3^3/_4$	4	$^1/_2$	$2^1/_4$	....
$1^1/_2$	6	$^{13}/_{16}$	$4^1/_2$	4	$^5/_8$	$2^1/_2$	....
2	$6^1/_2$	$^7/_8$	5	4	$^5/_8$	$2^1/_2$	....
$2^1/_2$	$7^1/_2$	1	$5^7/_8$	4	$^3/_4$	3	....
3	$8^1/_4$	$1^1/_8$	$6^5/_8$	8	$^3/_4$	$3^1/_4$	....
$3^1/_2$	9	$1^3/_{16}$	$7^1/_4$	8	$^3/_4$	$3^1/_4$	....
4	10	$1^1/_4$	$7^7/_8$	8	$^3/_4$	$3^1/_2$	....
$4^1/_2$	$10^1/_2$	$1^5/_{16}$	$8^1/_2$	8	$^3/_4$	$3^1/_2$	....
5	11	$1^3/_8$	$9^1/_4$	8	$^3/_4$	$3^3/_4$	....
6	$12^1/_2$	$1^7/_{16}$	$10^5/_8$	12	$^3/_4$	$3^3/_4$	....
7	14	$1^1/_2$	$11^7/_8$	12	$^7/_8$	4	....
8	15	$1^5/_8$	13	12	$^7/_8$	$4^1/_4$	....
9	$16^1/_4$	$1^3/_4$	14	12	1	$4^3/_4$	....
10	$17^1/_2$	$1^7/_8$	$15^1/_4$	16	1	5	....
12	$20^1/_2$	2	$17^3/_4$	16	$1^1/_8$	$5^1/_2$	....
14	23	$2^1/_8$	$20^1/_4$	20	$1^1/_8$	$5^3/_4$	....
15	$24^1/_2$	$2^3/_{16}$	$21^1/_2$	20	$1^1/_4$	6	....
16	$25^1/_2$	$2^1/_4$	$22^1/_2$	20	$1^1/_4$	6	....
18	28	$2^3/_8$	$24^3/_4$	24	$1^1/_4$	$6^1/_4$	....
20	$30^1/_2$	$2^1/_2$	27	24	$1^3/_8$	$6^3/_4$	....
22	33	$2^5/_8$	$29^1/_4$	24	$1^1/_2$	7	....
24	36	$2^3/_4$	32	24	$1^5/_8$	$7^1/_2$	$9^1/_2$
26	$38^1/_4$	$2^{13}/_{16}$	$34^1/_2$	28	$1^5/_8$	8	10
28	$40^3/_4$	$2^{15}/_{16}$	37	28	$1^5/_8$	8	10
30	43	3	$39^1/_2$	28	$1^3/_4$	$8^1/_2$	$10^1/_2$
32	$45^1/_4$	$3^1/_8$	$41^1/_2$	28	$1^7/_8$	9	11
34	$47^1/_2$	$3^1/_4$	$43^1/_2$	28	$1^7/_8$	9	$11^1/_2$
36	50	$3^3/_8$	46	32	$1^7/_8$	$9^1/_2$	$11^1/_2$
38	$52^1/_4$	$3^7/_{16}$	48	32	$1^7/_8$	$9^1/_2$	$11^1/_2$
40	$54^1/_2$	$3^9/_{16}$	$50^1/_4$	36	$1^7/_8$	10	12
42	57	$3^{11}/_{16}$	$52^3/_4$	36	$1^7/_8$	10	12
44	$59^1/_4$	$3^3/_4$	55	36	2	$10^1/_2$	$12^1/_2$
46	$61^1/_2$	$3^7/_8$	$57^1/_4$	40	2	$10^1/_2$	13
48	65	4	$60^3/_4$	40	2	11	13

Complete tables of sizes and dimensions of piping, valves, fittings, etc., are given in the Handbook on Piping referred to in Art. 176.

182. Piping Drawings.—There are several kinds of piping drawings, depending upon the purpose and requirements of the work. Sometimes a freehand sketch is sufficient, sometimes a line diagram, and sometimes a large scale drawing, consisting of several views of the entire system, together with working drawings of details is necessary. A drawing for construction purposes must give complete information as to sizes, posi-

tion of valves, branches and outlets. A drawing to show the layout of
existing pipe lines need not be as complete and is often made to small
scale, using single lines to represent the pipe with notes to tell sizes,
location and purpose for which the pipe is used. A drawing to show
proposed changes should give both existing and proposed piping, using

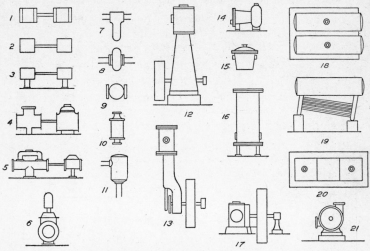

Fig. 230. Diagrams of Apparatus.

different kinds of lines to distinguish the changes. Dot and dash lines,
dash lines, or red or other colored ink may be used for this purpose. A
drawing for repairs may consist of simply the part to be repaired, or
may show the location or connection between the repairs and apparatus
or other parts of the system. Drawings for repairs should be checked
very carefully and just what is to be replaced or repaired should be made
clear.

183. Most of the general rules for dimensioning drawings hold for
piping plans, but there are a few points which may be mentioned. Always give figures to the centers of pipe, valves and fittings, and let the
pipe fitters make the necessary allowances. If a pipe is to be left un-
threaded, it is well to place a note on the drawing calling attention to
the fact. If left-hand (L. H.) threads are wanted it should be noted
Wrought pipe sizes can generally be given in a note using the nominal
sizes.

Flanged valves when drawn to large scale may have the over all dimensions given, the distance from center to top of hand wheel or valve stem

when open and when closed, diameter of hand wheel, etc. Separate flanges should be completely dimensioned as should all special parts. It is necessary that the location of the piping should be definitely given, which means that the parts of the building containing the piping must be shown and must be accurately dimensioned. The location of apparatus and the pipe connections should be given by measurements from the center lines of the machines, distances between centers of machines, heights of connections, etc.

Final drawings should be made after the engines, boilers and other machinery have been decided upon, as they can then be drawn completely and accurately. At least two views should be drawn, a plan and elevation. Often extra elevations and detail drawings are necessary. Every fitting and valve should be shown. A scale of $^3/_8$ inches equals 1 foot is desirable for piping drawings when it can be used, as it is large enough to show the system to scale.

184. Piping Sketches.—Sketching is an invaluable aid as a preliminary step in any kind of drawing, and a sketch is often the only

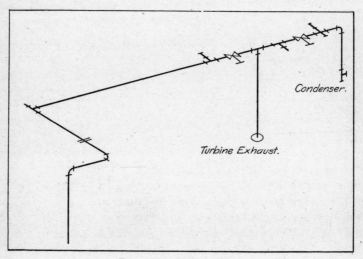

Fig. 231.   Pictorial View.

drawing needed. One's idea can be made clear and the number and kind of fittings and valves checked up in this way. Where only a small amount of work is to be done, a sketch may be made and fully dimensioned, from which a list of pieces can be made with lengths, sizes, etc. This will avoid mistakes in cutting, and the sketch shows just how the parts go together without depending upon memory. Such a sketch may be used to order with, but in such cases it should be made upon tracing cloth or thin paper so that a blue print can be made as a record. An H or 2H pencil will give lines black enough to print if ink is not used. The figures, however, should be put on in ink in all cases. If only one

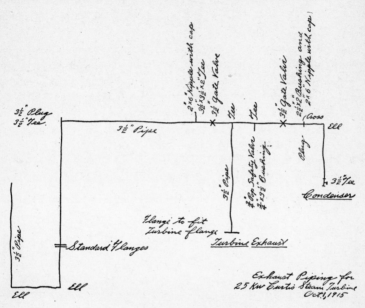

Fig. 232. Developed Sketch.

or two copies are wanted carbon paper may be used. Dimensions and notes should be put on as carefully as on a finished drawing. The general procedure is much the same as for all kinds of sketching. First sketch the arrangement using a single line diagram. When satisfactory the real sketch may be started by drawing the center lines, estimating locations of fittings, valves, etc., which should be spaced in roughly in proportion to their actual positions. The piping, valves, etc., can then be sketched in, using any of the conventions shown in Figs. 228 and 229. Finally locate dimension lines, figures and notes, together with the date and a title of some kind. Pictorial methods can be used to great advantage for sketching purposes, especially for preliminary layouts, as the directions and changes in levels can be clearly shown.

185. Developed or Single Plane Drawings.—It will often be found convenient to swing the various parts of a piping layout into a single

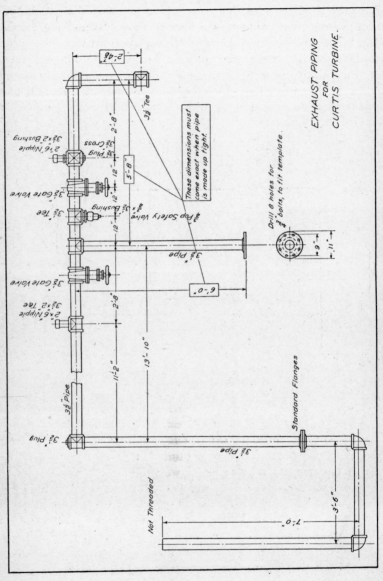

FIG. 233.   Developed Piping Drawing.

plane in order to show the various lengths and fittings in one view.   Different methods of showing the same piping are here illustrated.   Fig.
231 is a pictorial view using single lines to show the position in space;
Fig. 232 is a developed line sketch with the sizes, fittings, etc., written
on, and Fig. 233 is a developed drawing with complete dimensions and
notes.   Such drawings are valuable when listing or making up an order
as well as for the pipe fitters to work from.   A freehand line sketch, as a
preliminary step in laying out a steam line, can often be made in this
way.

CHAPTER XI

186. Preliminary Instructions.—A thorough understanding of the graphic language—the language of engineering—can be had only by applying it to a large number of problems. The problems in this chapter are sufficient to allow changes in the course given from year to year. The subjects as arranged follow the text in a general way and suggest the outline for a course. Since working directions are given for each problem the order of presenting them can be varied at the discretion of the instructor.

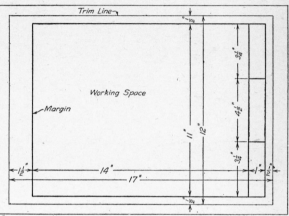

FIG. 234. Standard Layout.

187. Most of the drawing studies can be worked in an 11″ x 14″ space, the layout for which is given in Fig. 234 or in a division of the space as indicated in Fig. 235. If 18″ x 24″ paper is used it will give

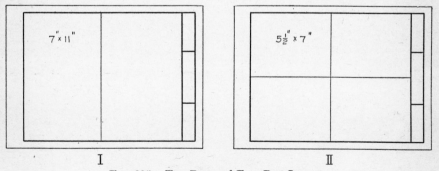

FIG. 235. Two Part and Four Part Layout.

two sheets with trim lines only at the ends. An inspection of the problem will indicate the proper space where it is not given in the statement of the problem. If a double size sheet is required the dimensions of Fig. 236 may be used.

Many of the problems given for a $5\frac{1}{2}''$ x $7''$ space can be worked to advantage in an $11''$ x $14''$ space by using a different scale or in a few cases by doubling all dimensions. A form of record strip is given in Fig. 237. Such a record strip should be a part of every drawing.

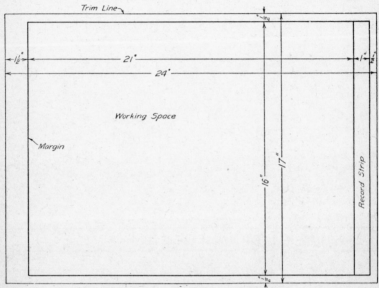

Fig. 236. Double Size Layout.

ELEMENTARY PRINCIPLES

188. The problems given in this section are intended for review purposes. It is not necessary to work all of them. Lay out the regular size sheet as shown in Fig. 234 and divide the working space into four equal spaces, $5\frac{1}{2}''$ x $7''$ each. Do not copy the dimensions given to locate views. Draw orthographic views. Do not copy the pictures which are used to present some of the problems.

PROB. 1, Fig. 238, Space I.—Draw three complete views of the RECTANGULAR STOP BAR.

PROB. 2, Fig. 238, Space II.—Draw three complete views of the GUIDE FOR SQUARE BAR.

NAME OF SCHOOL CITY OR TOWN	GENERAL TITLE Scale Date	SHEET NO. Drawn by Checked by Approved by

Fig. 237. Record Strip Form.

PROB. 3, Fig. 238, Space III.—Draw three complete views of the POSITIONING BLOCK. (Orthographic Projection.)

PROB. 4, Fig. 238, Space IV.—Draw three complete views of the SPECIAL DIE.

PROB. 5, Fig. 239, Space I.—Draw three complete views of the SLIDER.

PROB. 6, Fig. 239, Space II.—Draw three complete views of the BRACE BLOCK.

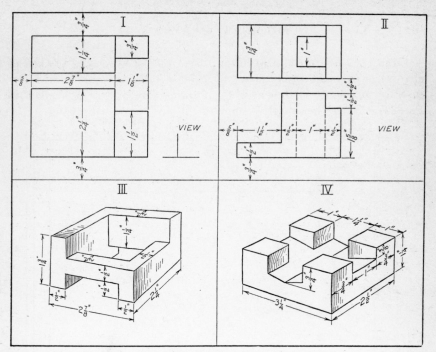

FIG. 238.   Probs. 1, 2, 3 and 4.

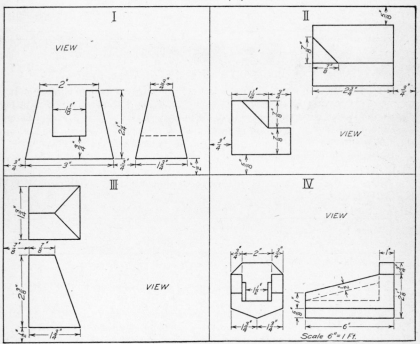

FIG. 239.   Probs. 5, 6, 7 and 8.

145

PROB. 7, Fig. 239, Space III.—Draw three complete views of the SPECIAL WEDGE.

PROB. 8, Fig. 239, Space IV.—Draw three complete views of the ADJUSTING SLIDE. Scale 6″ = 1 ft.

PROB. 9, Fig. 240, Space I.—Draw three complete views of the LUG.

PROB. 10, Fig. 240, Space II.—Draw three complete views of the ROD CLAMP.

PROB. 11, Fig. 240, Space III.—Draw three complete views of the CHAMFERED LOCK WASHER.

PROB. 12, Fig. 240, Space IV.—Draw three complete views of the LOCKING CATCH.

PROB. 13, Fig. 241.—The picture shows a SLIDING BRACE. Lay out a sheet with 11″ x 14″ working space (Fig. 234). Make a three view working drawing. Plan the arrangement and spacing of views by making a freehand sketch which should be submitted to the instructor.

PROB. 14, Fig. 242.—The picture shows a SADDLE PIVOT. Lay out a sheet with 11″ x 14″ working space. Make a three view working drawing.

PROB. 15, Fig. 243.—The illustration shows the *top, front* and *left end* views of a BRACKET. Make a three view drawing showing the *front, bottom* and *right end* views.

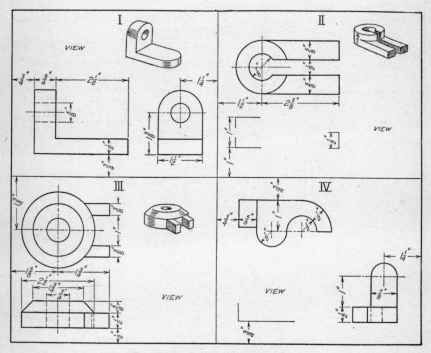

Fig. 240. Probs. 9, 10, 11 and 12.

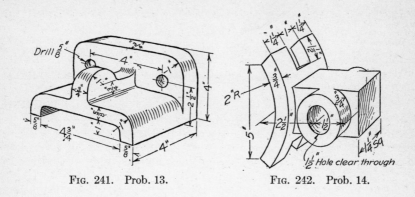

Fig. 241. Prob. 13.   Fig. 242. Prob. 14.

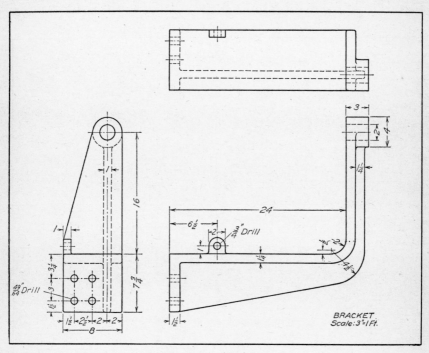

Fig. 243. Prob. 15.

189. Auxiliary Views.—Center or reference lines are shown on the layouts for the following problems. Draw auxiliary view of cut face only or of whole object as required by the instructor. Refer to Art. 19 and note which case covers each problem.

PROB. 16, Fig. 244, Space I.—Draw views given and auxiliary view.

PROB. 17, Fig. 244, Space II.—Draw views given and auxiliary view.

PROB. 18, Fig. 244, Space III.—Draw views given and auxiliary view.

PROB. 19, Fig. 244, Space IV.—Draw views given and auxiliary view.

PROB. 20, Fig. 245.—Draw the two views shown and an auxiliary view of the FOOT PEDAL. Front view is to be complete. Top and auxiliary views will be partial views. Do not put the location dimensions on your drawing. (11″ x 14″ space.)

PROB. 21, Fig. 246.—Draw the view shown and as much as may be necessary of the other two views indicated, for the ANGLE JOINT (11″ x 14″ space).

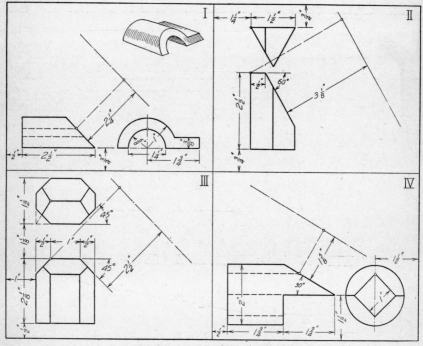

Fig. 244. Probs. 16, 17, 18 and 19.

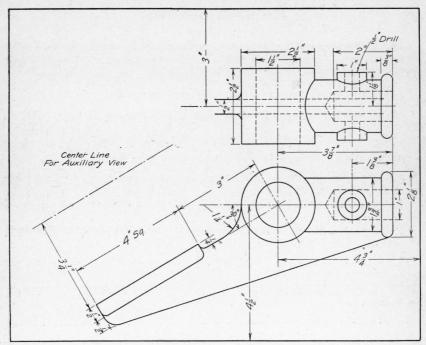

FIG. 245. Prob. 20.

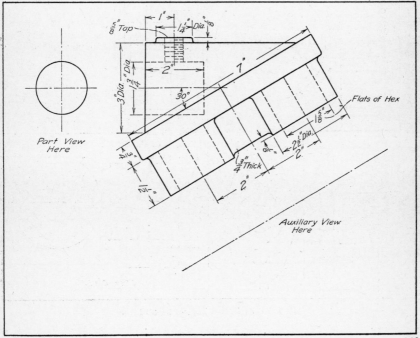

FIG. 246. Prob. 21.

190. Sectional Views.—The following problems are for the study of sectional views. Do not copy the views as given but make the required sectional views directly on your drawing.　Indicate the cut surface by section lining.

PROB. 22, Fig. 247, Space I.—Draw two views of the BUSHING.　Left hand view in section.

PROB. 23, Fig. 247, Space II.—Draw two views of the SPECIAL COLLAR. Left hand view in section.

PROB. 24, Fig. 247, Space III.—Draw two views of the GLAND.　Left hand view in section.

PROB. 25, Fig. 247, Space IV.—Draw two views of the SHIFTING COLLAR. Left hand view in section.

PROB. 26, Fig. 248, Space I.—Draw two views of the PISTON with right hand view in section.

PROB. 27, Fig. 248, Space II.—Draw two views of the PISTON FOLLOWER with left hand view in section.

PROB. 28, Fig. 248, Space III.—Draw two views of the ECCENTRIC with the left hand view in section.

PROB. 29, Fig. 248, Space IV.—Draw two views of the PULLEY, with the right hand view in section.

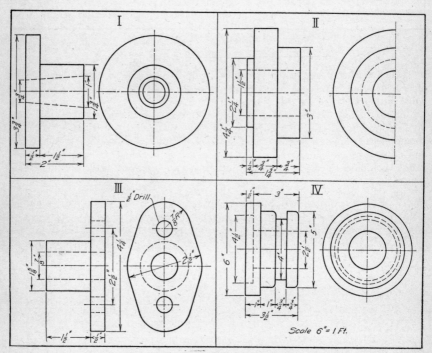

FIG. 247.　Probs. 22, 23, 24 and 25.

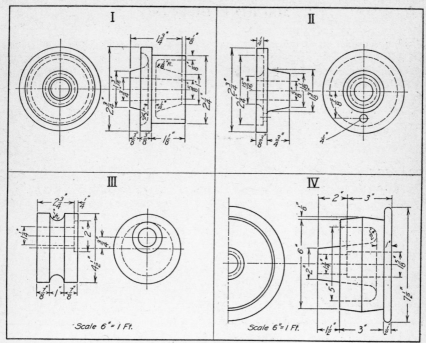

FIG. 248. Probs. 26, 27, 28 and 29.

SCREWS AND BOLTS

191. The Helix.—A cylindrical helix is a curve generated by a point on the surface of a cylinder, moving equal distances lengthwise of the cylinder while it is moving equal distances around the cylinder.

In Fig. 249 the diameter and pitch of the helix are indicated. Divide the circle of the top view into any convenient number of equal parts, and draw vertical lines through each point. Divide the pitch distance into the same number of equal parts and draw horizontal lines through each point. The intersection of a horizontal line from a division of the pitch distance with a vertical line from the corresponding division

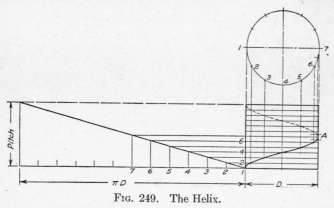

FIG. 249. The Helix.

x

151

of the circle will locate a point on the projection of the helix. Proceed in this way for each of the points. It is desirable to locate extra points by taking half divisions where the curve changes direction as at A.

192. Screws and Bolts.—The following problems are representative. The student should solve them with as little help as possible after studying the text. The proportions and appearances of the screw threads and bolts occur so frequently that they should be familiar without looking them up every time they occur on a drawing.

PROB. 30, Fig. 250.—Draw $1\frac{1}{2}$ turns of a right hand helix. Pitch $2''$. Diameter $2''$. (Space $5\frac{1}{2}'' \times 7''$.)

PROB. 31, Fig. 250.—Draw $1\frac{1}{2}$ turns of a left hand helix. Pitch $2''$. Diameter $2''$. (Space $5\frac{1}{2}'' \times 7''$.)

PROB. 32, Fig. 250.—Draw four forms of screw threads in section as directed by instructor. Pitch $1''$. (Space $7'' \times 11''$.)

PROB. 33, Fig. 251, Space I.—Draw three conventional representations of screw threads.

PROB. 34, Fig. 251, Space II.—Draw three conventional representations of threaded holes in plan and elevation as shown.

PROB. 35, Fig. 251, Space III.—Draw the stud and threaded rod ends as shown.

PROB. 36, Fig. 251, Space IV.—Draw three conventional representations of threaded holes in plan and section as shown.

PROB. 37, Fig. 252.—Draw accurately, a $1\frac{1}{2}''$ bolt, $10''$ long, with hex head and nut. Give specification dimensions as shown.

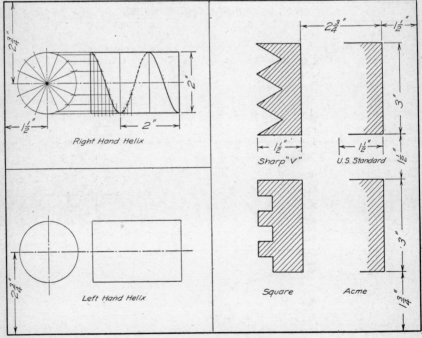

FIG. 250. Probs. 30, 31 and 32.

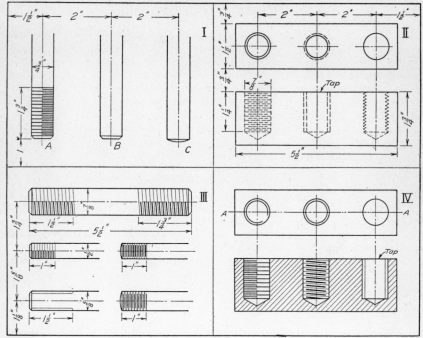

FIG. 251. Probs. 33, 34, 35 and 36.

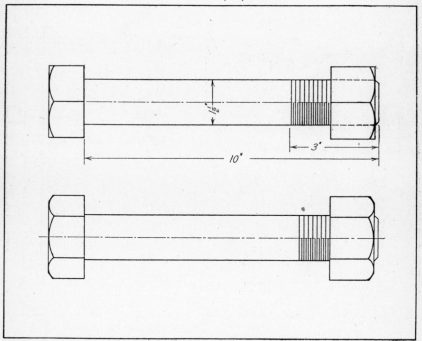

FIG. 252. Prob. 37, U. S. Std. Bolt.

PROB. 38, Fig. 253.—Make a drawing of the bolts, studs, etc., as shown in the figure. Give specification dimensions.

PROB. 39, Fig. 254, Space I.—On axis A–B draw a $3/4''$ through bolt, hex head across corners and hex nut across flats. On axis C–D draw a $1^1/s''$ bolt, hex head across flats and hex nut across corners. Give specification dimensions.

PROB. 40, Fig. 254, Space II.—On axis A–B draw a $7/8''$ bolt, square head across corners and square nut across flats. On axis C–D draw a $7/8''$ cap screw hex head across flats. On axis E–F draw a $7/8''$ cap screw hex head across corners.

PROB. 41, Fig. 254, Space III.—Draw two views of collar and shaft. On axis A–B draw a $5/8''$ set screw, head across flats. On axis C–D draw same set screw, head across corners.

PROB. 42, Fig. 254, Space IV.—Draw gland and stuffing box. On axis A–B draw a $1/2''$ stud and nut. Show nut across flats. Make provision for the gland to enter one half the depth of the stuffing box when nut is screwed onto stud. Show specification dimensions.

PROB. 43.—Lay out $11'' \times 14''$ working space. Draw a $1^3/4''$ hex nut across flats and a $1^3/4''$ square nut across corners. Compare them as to appearance and distance required for turning. Draw a $1^3/4''$ hex nut across corners and a $1^3/4''$ square nut across flats. Compare them.

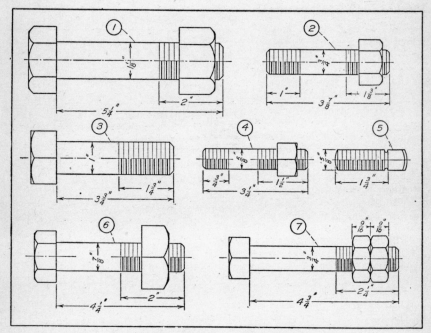

FIG. 253.   Prob. 38.   Bolt Drawing.

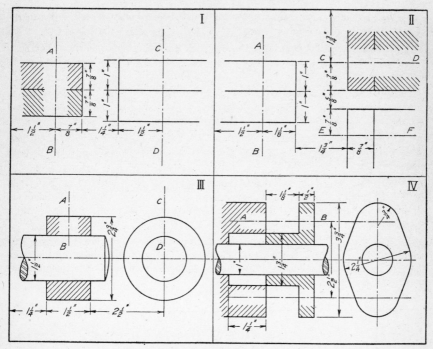

FIG. 254. Probs. 39, 40, 41 and 42.

MACHINE DRAWING REPRESENTATIONS

193. The following problems are planned for an 11" x 14" working space. Plan the arrangement, spacing, and choice of views, by making a freehand sketch which should be submitted to the instructor. The treatment of the views should have very careful attention and frequent reference should be made to the text of Chap. III for comparison with the illustrations there given.

PROB. 44, Fig. 255.—The picture shows a FORKED LEVER. Make a detail working drawing.

PROB. 45, Fig. 256.—Make a detail working drawing of the ANGLE BRACE BEARING.

PROB. 46, Fig. 257.—Make a working drawing of the STIRRUP.

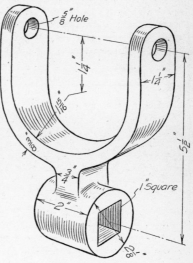

FIG. 255. Prob. 44.

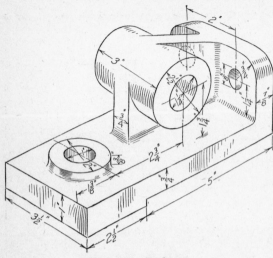

FIG. 256.   Prob. 45.

PROB. 47, Fig. 258.— Make a working drawing of the ADJUSTABLE GUIDE. Note the method of laying out the top view. Do not copy the picture.

PROB. 48, Fig. 259.— The front, top, and right end views of a COLUMN GUIDE are shown. Draw the front *bottom* and right end view as a section.

PROB. 49, Fig. 260.— Make a three view working drawing of the CLAMP PIECE. Do not use the top and front views which are given but show the piece in such a position that the views will not contain so many dotted lines.

PROB. 50, Fig. 261.—Draw the top view and a section of the SUPPORT.

PROB. 51, Fig. 262.—Make a working drawing of the HEAD PLATE. Show the right hand view as a section.

PROB. 52, Fig. 263.—Make a three view assembly drawing of the STEP BEARING. Show the front view as a half section. Scale 6″ = 1 ft.

PROB. 53, Fig. 263.—Make a separate detail drawing of each part of the STEP BEARING. 11″ x 14″ working space. Scale 6″ = 1 ft.

PROB. 54, Fig. 264.—Make an assembly working drawing of the FOUNDATION BOLT PLATE. Show the front view as a section. The top and right side views can be represented as shown. Look up dimensions of 2″ pipe.

PROB. 55, Fig. 265.—Make a working drawing of the VALVE. Show the right hand view with proper treatment as a section.

PROB. 56, Fig. 266.—Make a working drawing of the ADJUSTING LEVER.

PROB. 57, Fig. 267, Space I.—Draw front view as section with proper treatment.

PROB. 58, Fig. 267, Space II.—Draw section on plane through axis.

PROB. 59, Fig. 267, Space III.—Represent the bent iron by proper views.

PROB. 60, Fig. 267, Space IV.—Draw a section on plane through axis.

PROB. 61, Fig. 268.—Make a working drawing of the LEVER.

PROB. 62, Fig. 269.—Draw two full views of the TRUNNION.

PROB. 63, Fig. 269.—Draw two views of the TRUNNION, one a section through the axis.

PROB. 64, Fig. 270.—Make working drawing of the T–SLOT LEVER. Completely dimension. Consider true distances and treatment of views. Submit a preliminary freehand sketch to your instructor.

PROB. 65, Fig. 271.—Draw two exterior views of LUG COLLAR.

PROB. 65-A, Fig. 271.—Make a working drawing of the LUG COLLAR. Show right hand view with proper view as a section.

PROB. 66, Fig. 272.—Make a working drawing of the SPREADER in full or section.

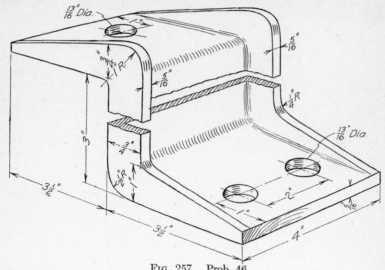

FIG. 257.   Prob. 46.

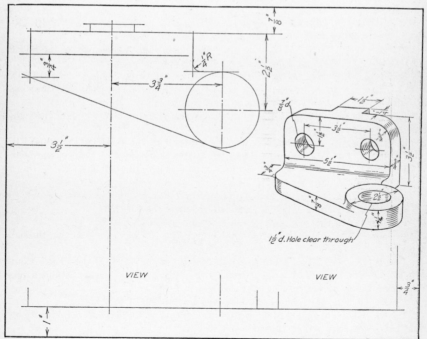

FIG. 258.   Prob. 47.

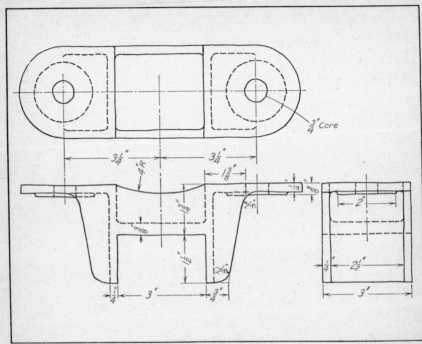

Fig. 259. Prob. 48.

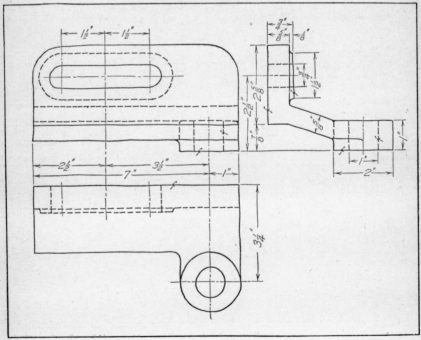

Fig. 260. Prob. 49.

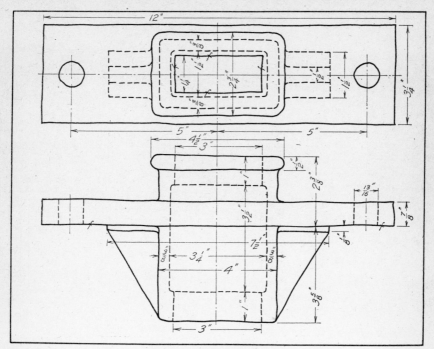

Fig. 261.   Prob. 50.

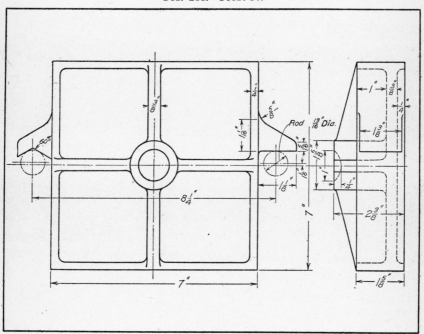

Fig. 262.   Prob. 51.

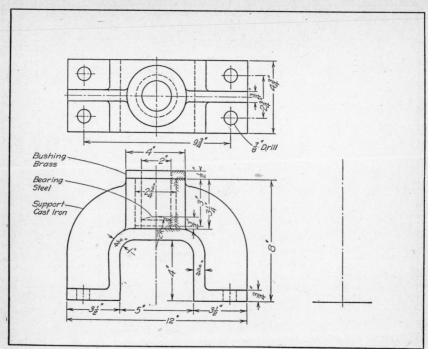

Bushing Brass
Bearing Steel
Support Cast Iron

FIG. 263. Probs. 52 and 53.

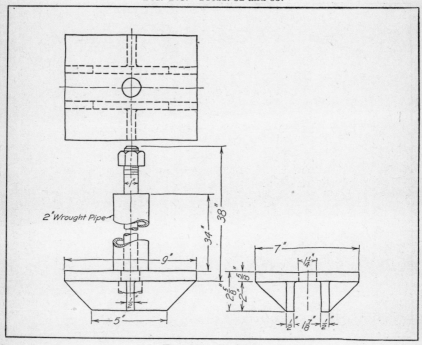

2" Wrought Pipe

FIG. 264. Prob. 54.

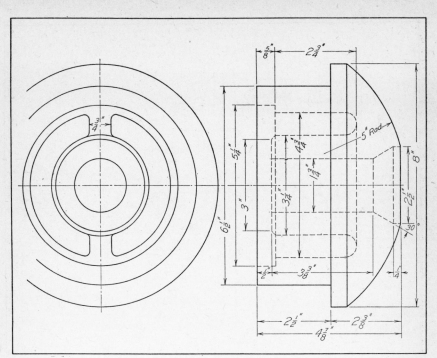

Fig. 265.   Prob. 55.

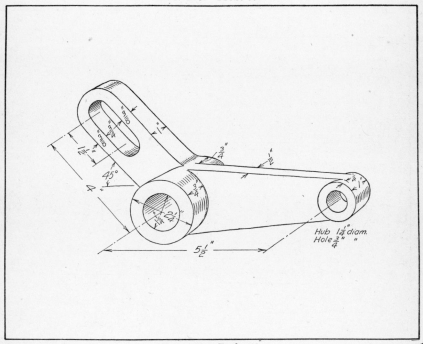

Fig. 266.   Prob. 56.

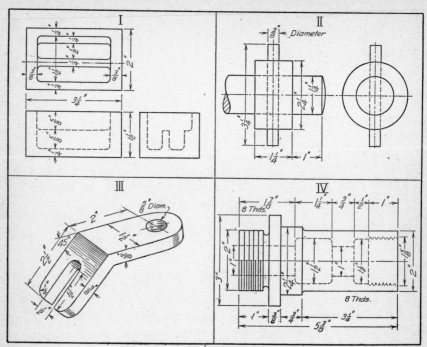

FIG. 267. Probs. 57, 58, 59 and 60.

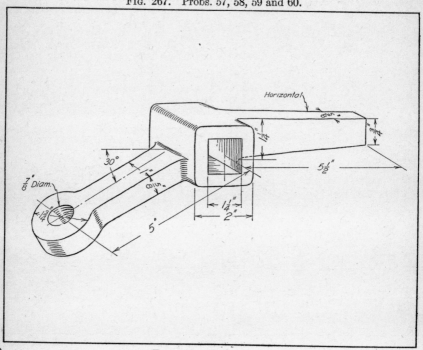

FIG. 268. Prob. 61.

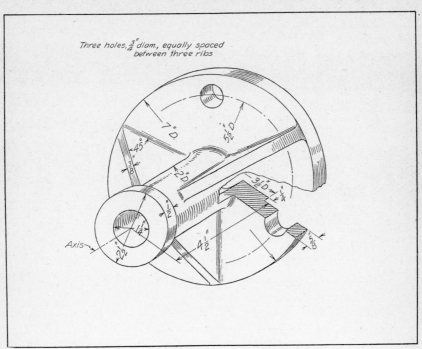

Three holes, $\frac{3}{4}$" diam., equally spaced
between three ribs

FIG. 269. Probs. 62 and 63.

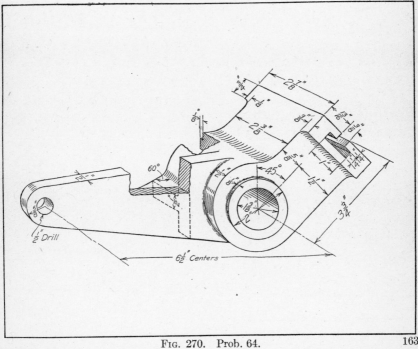

FIG. 270. Prob. 64.

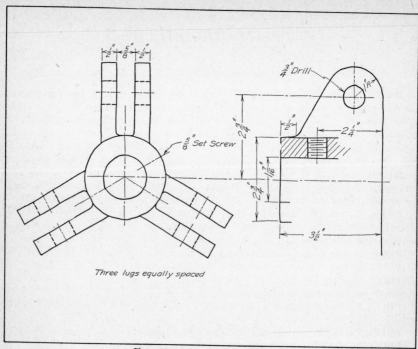

FIG. 271. Probs. 65 and 65-A.

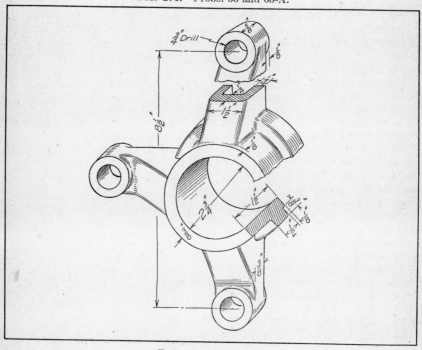

FIG. 272. Prob. 66.

DIMENSIONING

194. The study of dimensioning will occur every time a working drawing is made· The rules and systems given in Chapter IV should be carefully studied, and their application observed. The location of finished surfaces and center lines must always be considered. Go slowly and give a reason for every dimension and for its location. Figures 274 and 275 are to be drawn from measurements obtained with the dividers and scale. Set your dividers on the drawing as at I, Fig. 273, and then place the points on the printed scale as at II when the reading shows the distance to be 1¹/₄″. Use 1¹/₄″ from your full size scale in laying out your drawing. Obtain other distances in the same way using dividers and the printed scale shown near the center of Figs. 274 and 275.

PROB. 67, Fig. 274, Space I.—Draw the two views of the DISTANCE PIECE, using the method just described. Scale your drawing to nearest ¹/₈″ and put on dimension lines and dimensions.

PROB. 68, Fig. 274, Space II.—Draw and dimension the views of the BUSHING.

PROB. 69, Fig. 274, Space III.—Draw and dimension the views of the SLIDE.

PROB. 60, Fig. 274, Space IV.—Draw the views of the CORNER CLAMP and dimension your drawing.

PROB. 71, Fig. 275, Space I.—Draw the views of the PROJECTING BEARING and dimension your drawing.

PROB. 72, Fig. 275, Space II.—Draw and dimension the views of the SUPPORT.

PROB. 73, Fig. 275, Space III.—Draw the views of the HUNG BEARING and dimension your drawing.

PROB. 74, Fig. 275, Space IV.—Draw and dimension the views of the GUIDE.

PROB. 75, Fig. 74, Chap. III.—Make a detail drawing of TYPE B MOTOR BEARING DETAILS. Show views as half sections instead of full sections as given.

PROB. 76, Fig. 82, Chap. III.—Make a two view drawing, both views in full for the PULLEY. Completely dimension.

PROB. 77, Fig. 82, Chap. III.—Make a two view drawing, one view in half section. Completely dimension.

PROB. 78, Fig. 86, Chap. III.—Make a two view drawing, both views in full for the VERTICAL GUIDE. There are 8 holes equally spaced in the flange. Completely dimension.

PROB. 79, Fig. 86, Chap. III.—Make a two view drawing, one view in section. Completely dimension.

PROB. 80, Fig. 87, Chap. III.—Make a three view drawing of the BOLSTER SUPPORT. Show views in full, section, or half section as directed by the instructor.

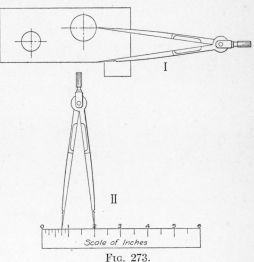

Scale of Inches

FIG. 273.

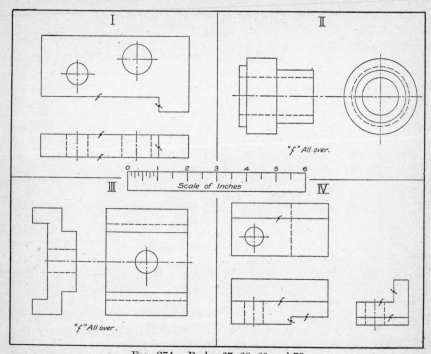

FIG. 274. Probs. 67, 68, 69 and 70.

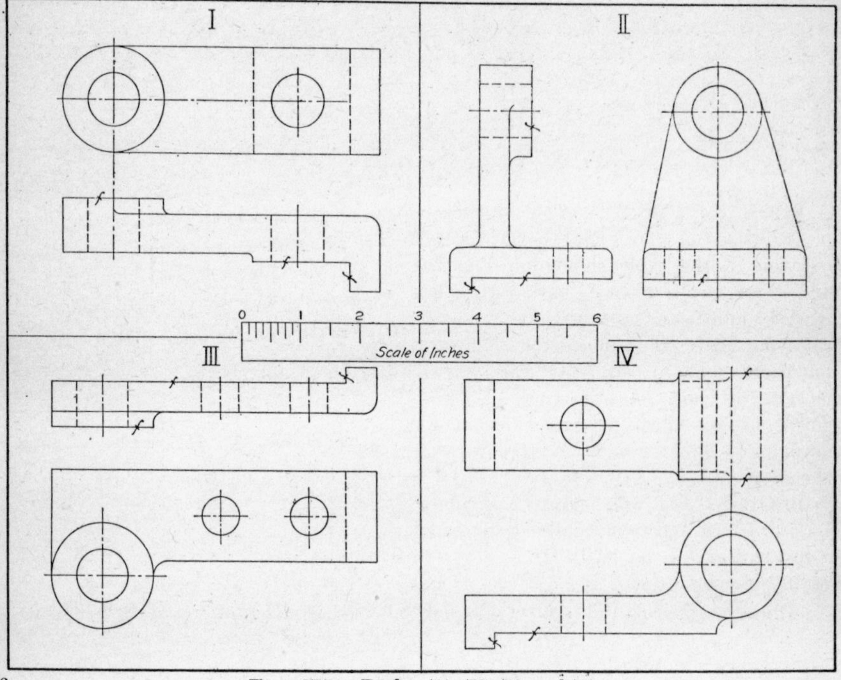

FIG. 275. Probs. 71, 72, 73 and 74.

195. Graphical Data.—Under certain conditions graphical methods may be used to determine dimensions of machines or parts. Problems 81 and 82 may be solved by this method. The equations for the straight lines or curves are sometimes worked out giving formulas for use in calculation. Refer to Art. 112 before working Problems 81 and 82.

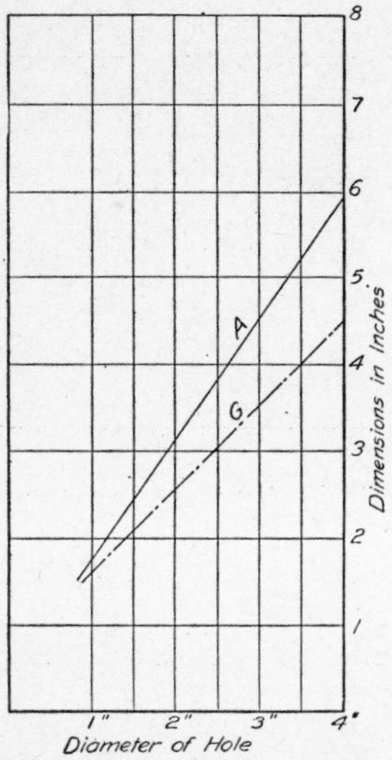

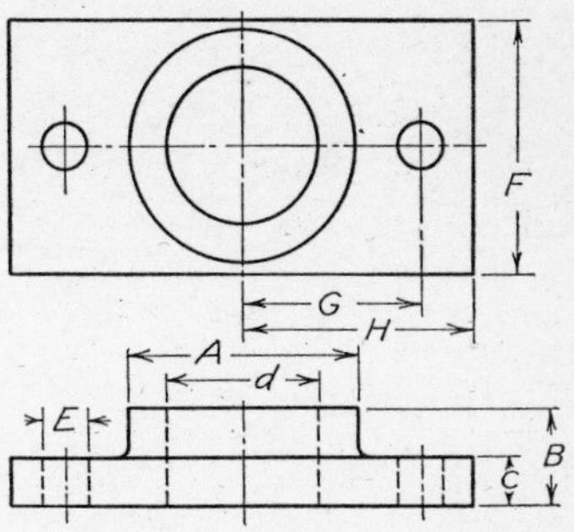

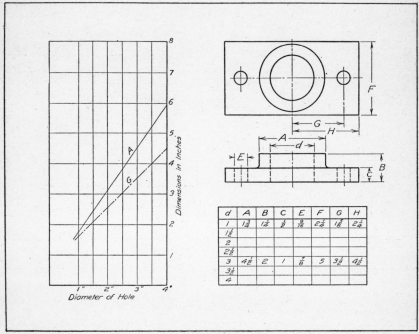

d	A	B	C	E	F	G	H
1	$1\frac{3}{4}$	$1\frac{1}{4}$	$\frac{1}{2}$	$\frac{9}{16}$	$2\frac{1}{4}$	$1\frac{5}{8}$	$2\frac{1}{4}$
$1\frac{1}{2}$							
2							
$2\frac{1}{2}$							
3	$4\frac{1}{2}$	2	1	$\frac{7}{8}$	5	$3\frac{1}{2}$	$4\frac{1}{2}$
$3\frac{1}{2}$							
4							

FIG. 276. Prob. 81.

PROB. 81, Fig. 276.—The dimensions for two sizes of the VERTICAL GUIDE are given in the table shown on Fig. 276. With these values draw a chart with a line for each dimension, as shown for A and G. Scale your chart and fill in the table with dimensions for each size. Indicate the dimensions by letters, on the views of a convenient size as shown. Derive a formula for one or more dimensions as directed by your instructor.

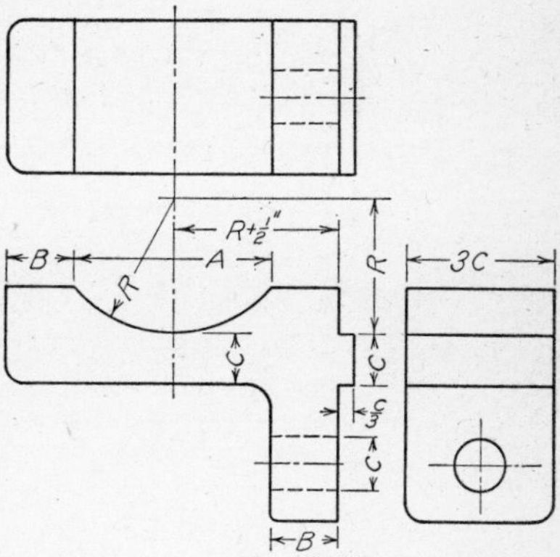

FIG. 277.

PROB. 82, Fig. 277.—Make a graphical chart, drawing, and table of dimensions similar to Fig. 276 for the SUPPORT shown in Fig. 277, for values of R of 1″, 2″, 3″ 4″ and 5″. Obtain sufficient values to plot graphical chart from equations which follow:

$$A = \sqrt{12R - R^2 - 7}, \qquad B = \frac{R}{4} + \frac{3''}{4}, \qquad C = \frac{3}{4}B.$$

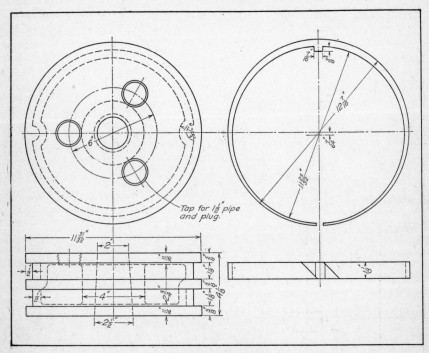

FIG. 278.   Prob. 83.

MACHINE DETAILS

196. The contents of Chap. V should be studied carefully while working the following problems. If reference books on Machine Design are available they should be consulted.

PROB. 83, Fig. 278.—Make a working drawing of the STEAM PISTON. Show one view as a half section.

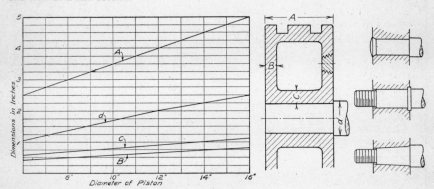

FIG. 279.   Piston Dimensions.

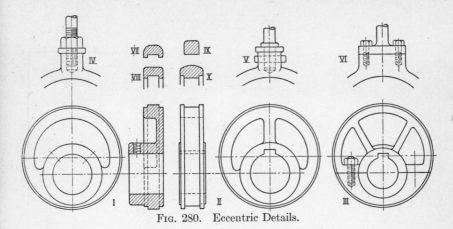

FIG. 280. Eccentric Details.

PROB. 84.—Make a complete two view working drawing for a steam engine piston. Material is cast iron. Diameter of cylinder is 8″. Hollow part of piston is divided into four sections by ribs. Piston rings ½″ wide and ¼″ thick. Obtain dimensions d, A, B, and C from diagram of Fig. 279. It will be necessary to provide a hole from each section of the piston to allow for support of cores. These holes can be tapped and closed with pipe plugs. There should be two shallow tapped holes in the head end of the piston into which rods can be screwed to remove the piston from the cylinder. Show method of fastening rod and piston (11″ x 14″ working space). Refer to Chapter V.

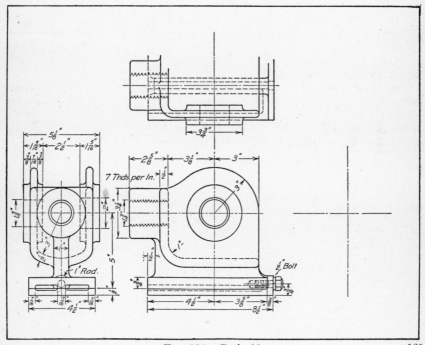

FIG. 281. Prob. 88.

PROB. 85.—Make a complete two view working drawing of a steam piston as described for Prob. 86 but diameter of cylinder = 14″ and piston rings ⁵/₈″ wide and ¹/₂″ thick. Divide hollow part of piston into six equal sections. Refer to Chapter V.

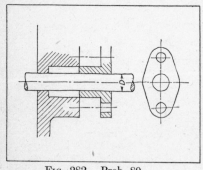

FIG. 282. Prob. 89.

FIG. 283. Prob. 90.

PROB. 86.—Make a working drawing for an eccentric sheave and straps for the diameter of shaft specified by the instructor. Dimensions not given in table are to be worked out on your drawing. Suggestions for design are given in Fig. 280. Make a sketch and submit for criticism before starting your drawing.

DIMENSIONS IN INCHES

Diameter of Shaft	$2\frac{1}{2}$	$2\frac{3}{4}$	3	8
Throw of Eccentric	$\frac{7}{8}$	1	$1\frac{1}{8}$	$2\frac{1}{4}$
Width of Eccentric	$1\frac{1}{2}$	$1\frac{5}{8}$	$1\frac{3}{4}$	$3\frac{1}{2}$
Diameter of Eccentric Rod	$\frac{3}{4}$	$\frac{7}{8}$	1	2
Diameter of Bolts	$\frac{1}{2}$	$\frac{9}{16}$	$\frac{5}{8}$	1 to $1\frac{1}{8}$

PROB. 87, Fig. 281.—Draw three views of the CROSSHEAD SHOE.

PROB. 88, Fig. 281.—Make a complete working drawing of the CROSSHEAD only. Show complete top, right end, and left end views in section.

PROB. 89, Fig. 282.— Make a drawing for a gland stuffing box—either plain or brass lined. Give complete dimensions for gland, box, and studs. Diameter of rod as specified by instructor. Study Art. 120.

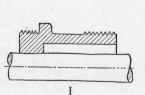

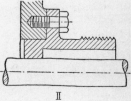

I

II

FIG. 284.

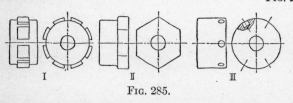

I

II

III

FIG. 285.

PROB. 90, Fig. 283. —Make assembly and detail drawings for a screw type STUFFING BOX. Diameter of rod as specified by instructor. Variations in the design of the body and gland nut are given in Figs. 284 and 285. See Art. 120.

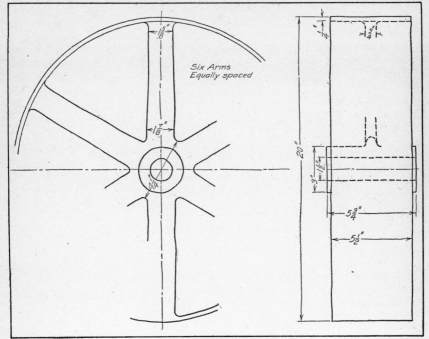

Six Arms
Equally spaced

FIG. 286. Prob. 95. C. I. Pulley.

BEARINGS AND PULLEYS

197. The following problems are based upon Chap. VI. Only the elements are considered and the question of design is left for books on Machine Design. The catalogs of transmission machinery manufacturers can be studied to advantage.

PROB. 91, Fig. 166, Chap. VI.—Make a working drawing of a solid BABBITTED BEARING. Size as specified by instructor.

PROB. 92, Fig. 167, Chap. VI.—Make a working drawing for size specified by instructor.

PROB. 93, Fig. 168, Chap. VI.—Make an outline drawing for size specified by instructor.

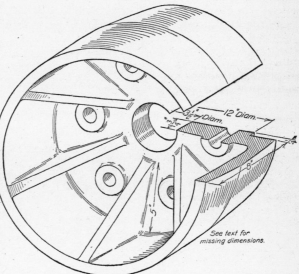

See text for
missing dimensions.

FIG. 287. **Prob. 96.** Special Pulley.

171

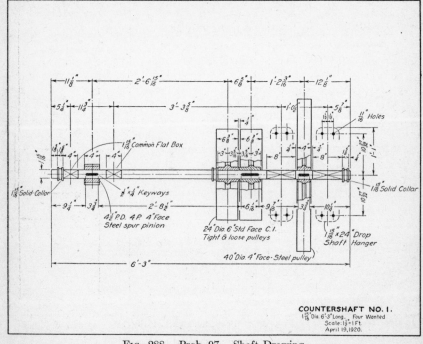

FIG. 288.   Prob. 97.   Shaft Drawing.

PROB. 94, Fig. 170, Chap. VI.—Make a drawing of POST BOX for size specified by instructor.

PROB. 95, Fig. 286.—Make a working drawing of the cast iron PULLEY.   Show
right hand view in section.

PROB. 96, Fig. 287.—Make a two view working drawing of the SPECIAL PULLEY.
Diameter of pulley is 16″.   There are six ribs ³/₄″ thick and six holes 1″ diameter
equally spaced on a 9″ bolt circle.   The bosses are 2¹/₈″ diameter and ¹/₄″ out from
surface.   Other dimensions are given on the figure.

SHAFTING AND COUPLINGS

198. The drawings for shafting layouts must be carefully checked.   Complete
details of standard bearings, pulleys, etc., are not necessary but sufficient information
should be given for purposes of ordering and erection.

PROB. 97, Fig. 288.—Make a complete shafting drawing as shown.

PROB. 98, Fig. 289.—Make a complete shafting drawing with all dimensions,
similar to Fig. 288, for the shaft shown in Fig. 289.   The smaller pulley is 16″ diameter
and the larger pulley 24″ diameter.   Get other dimensions from the tables given in
Chap. VI.

PROB. 99, Fig. 184, Chap. VII.—Make a drawing for a SOLID SLEEVE COUP-
LING for size specified by instructor.

PROB. 100, Fig. 185, Chap. VII.—Make a drawing for a CLAMP COUPLING
for size specified by instructor.

PROB. 101, Fig. 186, Chap. VII.—Make a drawing for a FLANGE COUPLING
for size specified by instructor.

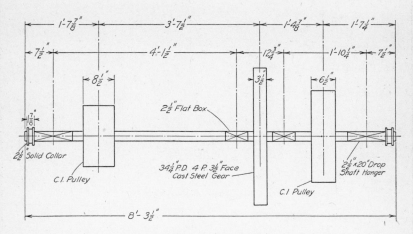

Fig. 289. Prob. 98. Shaft Drawing.

JIGS AND FIXTURES

199. The following problems emphasize points to be considered in shop drafting.

PROB. 102, Fig. 291.—
Make a working drawing for
the MAIN CASTING of a
jig for the LINK of Fig. 290.
The letters A, B, C, etc., are
for reference when making an
assembly. Dimensions not
given are to be worked out by
the student. Refer to Fig. 292.

PROB. 103, Fig. 292.—
Draw the JIG DETAILS.
Refer to Figs. 290, 291 and to
Chap. VIII. Use standard
bushings as dimensioned in
Table 23, Chap. VIII.

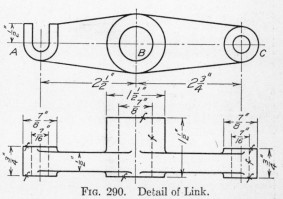

Fig. 290. Detail of Link.

PROB. 104, Figs. 290, 291, and 292.—Make an assembled jig drawing showing the
piece to be drilled in its position in the jig. The drawing should be similar to Fig. 189.
Letters A, B, C on Fig. 290 are also given on Fig. 291 to indicate position of the LINK.
The LOCATING PIN is put in place at A and the HAND SCREW screws through
the tapped hole E and holds the link against the locating pin. The SCREW BUSHING
and $7/8''$ SLIP BUSHING go in place at B. The screw bushing presses against the link.
The LINER BUSHING and $7/16''$ SLIP BUSHING are used at C. The V–BLOCK is
held against the end of the link marked C by the SCREW and HANDWHEEL. The
screw stem passes through the PLATE. The plate is held at D by countersunk screws.

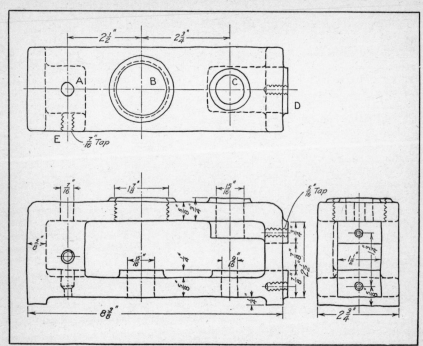

FIG. 291.   Probs. 102 and 104.

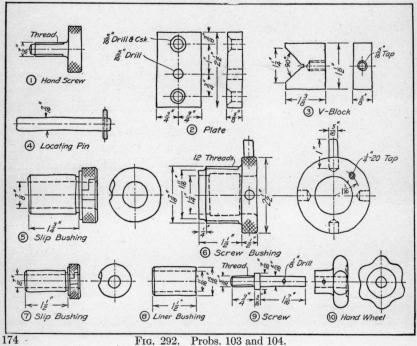

FIG. 292.   Probs. 103 and 104.

PROB. 105, Figs. 190 and 191, Chap. IX.— Make a working drawing for the details of the FIXTURE. Show each part separately. Obtain dimensions by use of dividers and the scale shown on the figure, by method described in Art. 194.

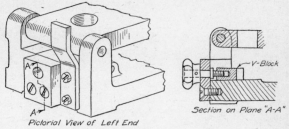

Pictorial View of Left End

Section on Plane "A-A"

FIG. 293. Probs. 102 to 104.

PROB. 106, Figs. 190 and 191, Chap. IX.— Make a drawing of the complete fixture with the *work* in place as in the figure. Obtain dimensions as described in Art. 194.

PROB. 107, Figs. 188 and 189, Chap. IX.—Make a drawing of the JIG as shown in the figure. Obtain dimensions by using dividers and the scale shown on the figure by method described in Art. 194. The sketches of Fig. 293 will help in reading Fig. 189.

PROB. 108, Figs. 188 and 189, Chap. IX.—Make a working drawing showing each of the details of the jig separately. Obtain dimensions as described in Art. 194.

GEARS AND CAMS

200. The following problems are suggestive and can be easily multiplied by modifying the conditions stated. For a complete study of the drafting of gears, see Anthony's Essentials of Gearing, D. C. Heath Co., Boston.

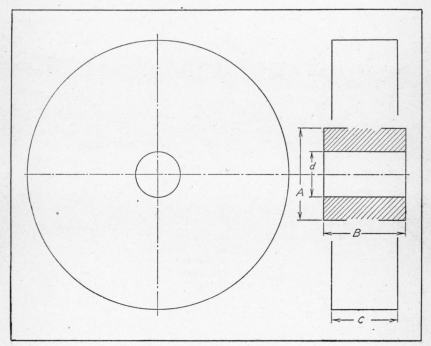

FIG. 294. Probs. 110 to 119.

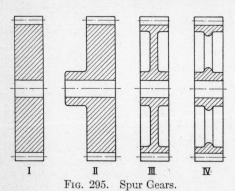

I   II   III   IV

FIG. 295.   Spur Gears.

PROB. 109, Fig. 204, Chap. IX.—Make a SPUR GEAR drawing as shown in Fig. 204.

PROB. 110, Fig. 294.—Make a SPUR GEAR drawing similar to Fig. 204 for conditions which follow. Four sections are shown in Fig. 295 where a plain gear is shown at I, plain with hub at II, webbed at III and with arms at IV. Various combinations can, of course, be made.

Details or dimensions not specified are to be worked out by the student on his drawing. Letters refer to Fig. 294. Solve problem using values given in the following table for gear specified by instructor. Choose scale so that gear can be drawn in 11″ x 14″ space.

PROB.	Pitch	Number of Teeth	A	B	C	D
110........	8	68	$2^1/_8$	$1^3/_8$	$1^1/_8$	$1^1/_{16}$
111........	7	62	$2^1/_4$	$1^1/_2$	$1^1/_4$	$1^1/_8$
112........	6	58	$2^1/_2$	2	$1^1/_2$	$1^1/_4$
113........	5	43	3	$2^1/_4$	$1^3/_4$	$1^1/_2$
114........	4	66	$3^1/_4$	$2^1/_2$	2	$1^5/_8$
115........	$3^1/_2$	64	4	3	$2^1/_2$	2
116........	3	28	$3^1/_2$	3	$2^1/_2$	$1^3/_4$
117........	$2^3/_4$	44	4	$3^1/_4$	$2^3/_4$	2
118........	$2^1/_4$	70	$5^1/_4$	$3^3/_4$	$3^1/_4$	$2^1/_4$
119........	2	30	$5^1/_2$	$4^1/_2$	4	$2^1/_2$

PROB. 120, Fig. 208, Chap. IX.—Make a BEVEL GEAR drawing as shown in Fig. 208 (11″ x 14″ space).

PROB. 121, Fig. 296.—Make a drawing for the MITRE GEAR suggested in Fig. 296. Give complete dimensions, angles, etc.

PROB. 122.—Make a drawing for a MITRE GEAR similar to the previous problem but for 6 pitch and 54 teeth. Use same size shaft and hub.

PROB. 123, Fig. 297.—Make a drawing for the WORM and WHEEL as shown in Fig. 297.

PROB. 124, Fig. 298.—Design a PLATE CAM with point contact (as in Fig. 212) to raise follower during one half revolution with uniform motion and allow it to drop during remaining half revolution with uniform motion.

$$x = 9'', \qquad y = 5'', \qquad AB = \text{rise} = 1^3/_4'', \qquad \text{Distance } OA = 2^3/_4''.$$

PROB. 125, Fig. 298.—PLATE CAM with point contact to raise follower during one third revolution, drop during one third revolution at rest during one third revolution. Uniform motion up and down.

$$x = 9'', \qquad y = 5'', \qquad AB = 2'', \qquad OA = 2^1/_2''.$$

PROB. 126, Fig. 298.—PLATE CAM with point contact. Motion as follows: Up 1 inch during $1/_4$ rev. with gravity motion. At rest during $1/_8$ rev. Up 1 inch during $1/_4$ rev. with gravity motion. Down 2 inches during $1/_4$ rev. with uniform motion. At rest during $1/_8$ rev.

$$x = 9'', \qquad y = 5'', \qquad AB = 2'', \qquad OA = 2^1/_2''.$$

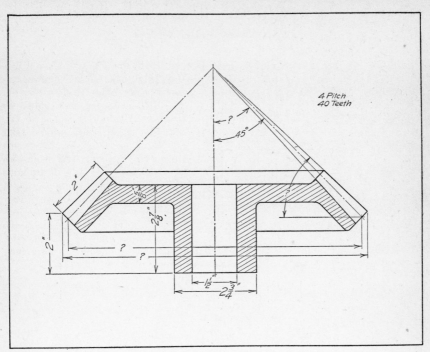

4 Pitch
40 Teeth

45°

Fig. 296. Prob. 121. Mitre Gears.

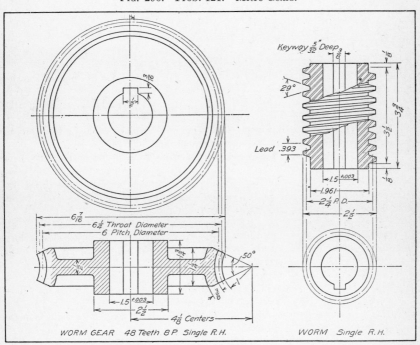

Keyway $\frac{5}{32}$" Deep

29°

Lead .393

1.5 ±.003

1.961

$2\frac{1}{4}$ P.D.

$2\frac{1}{2}$

WORM Single R.H.

$6\frac{7}{16}$

$6\frac{1}{4}$ Throat Diameter

6 Pitch Diameter

50°

1.5 ±.003

$2\frac{1}{2}$

$4\frac{1}{8}$ Centers

WORM GEAR 48 Teeth 8 P. Single R.H.

Fig. 297. Prob. 123. Worm and Wheel.

177

PROB. 127, Fig. 298.—PLATE CAM with point contact. Motion as follows: Up $1\frac{1}{2}$ inches during $\frac{1}{3}$ rev. with harmonic motion at rest during $\frac{1}{6}$ rev. Drop $1\frac{1}{2}$ inches during $\frac{1}{3}$ rev. with harmonic motion. At rest during $\frac{1}{6}$ rev.

$$x = 9'', \qquad y = 5'', \qquad AB = 1\frac{1}{2}'', \qquad OA = 3\frac{1}{4}''.$$

PROB. 129, Fig. 298.—PLATE CAM with roller $\frac{3}{4}$ inches diameter. Same motion as for Prob. 124. $\quad x = 9'', \qquad y = 5'', \qquad AB = 1\frac{3}{4}'', \qquad OA = 2\frac{3}{4}''.$

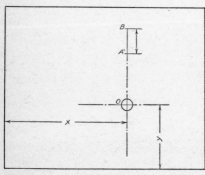

Fig. 298.

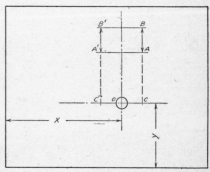

Fig. 299.

PROB. 129, Fig. 298.—PLATE CAM with roller $\frac{3}{4}$ inches diameter. Same motion as for Prob. 125. $\quad x = 9'', \qquad y = 5'', \qquad AB = 2'', \qquad OA = 2\frac{1}{2}''.$

PROB. 130, Fig. 298.—PLATE CAM with roller $\frac{3}{4}$ inches diameter. Same motion as for Prob. 127. $\quad x = 9'', \qquad y = 5'', \qquad AB = 1\frac{1}{2}'', \qquad OA = 3\frac{1}{4}''.$

PROB. 131, Fig. 299.—Design a PLATE CAM with *point* or *roller* contact as directed by instructor. Motion as follows: Up $1\frac{3}{4}$ inches during $\frac{1}{2}$ rev. with uniform motion. Down $1\frac{3}{4}$ inches during $\frac{1}{2}$ rev. with uniform motion. Shaft revolves left hand.

$$x = 9'', \qquad y = 5'', \qquad AB = 1\frac{3}{4}'', \qquad CA = 2\frac{1}{2}'', \qquad OC = 1\frac{1}{4}''.$$

PROB. 132, Fig. 299.—Same as Prob. 131 except,

$$x = 9'', \qquad y = 5'', \qquad A'B' = 1\frac{1}{2}'', \qquad C'A' = 3'', \qquad OC' = 1''.$$

PROB. 133, Fig. 299.—PLATE CAM with either point or roller contact. Motion as follows: Up during $\frac{1}{3}$ rev. with gravity motion. Down during $\frac{1}{3}$ rev. with gravity motion. Rest during $\frac{1}{3}$ rev. $x = 9'', \; y = 5'', \; AB = 1\frac{3}{4}'', \; CA = 2\frac{1}{2}'', \; OC = 1\frac{3}{8}''.$

PROB. 134, Fig. 299.—PLATE CAM. Same as Prob. 131, harmonic motion.

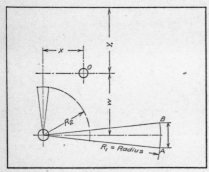

Fig. 300.

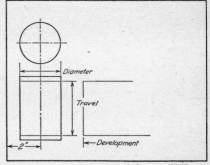

Fig. 301.

PROB. 135, Fig. 298.—PLATE CAM with flat follower (as in Fig. 217). Motion and distances as in Prob. 120 except $x = 7''$.

PROB. 136, Fig. 298.—PLATE CAM with flat follower. Motion and distances as follows: Up during $1/3$ rev. with harmonic motion. At rest $1/6$ rev. Down during $1/3$ rev. with gravity motion. At rest $1/6$ rev. Dimensions as for Prob. 129.

PROB. 137, Fig. 300.—Design a PLATE CAM similar to Fig. 216. Show cam outline complete. Motion as follows: Up from A to B during $1/2$ rev. with gravity motion. Drop from B to A during $1/4$ rev. with gravity motion. At rest during $1/4$ rev.

$$W = 5'', \qquad x = 2^1/_2'', \qquad y = 3^1/_2'', \qquad AB = 3'', \qquad R_1 = 10'', \qquad R_2 = 3^1/_2''.$$

PROB. 138, Fig. 300.—Same as Prob. 137 but for uniform motion.

PROB. 139, Fig. 301.—Draw the development of the pitch line for a CYLIN-DRICAL CAM (as in Fig. 219) for the following motion.

Parallel to axis $2^1/_2$ inches during $1/3$ rev. with harmonic motion. At rest $1/6$ rev. Return parallel to axis $2^1/_2$ inches during $1/4$ rev. with harmonic motion. At rest $1/4$ rev. Diameter $= 3''$. Travel $= 2^1/_2''$.

PROB. 140, Fig. 301.—Same as Prob. 139 but for gravity motion and show groove for $3/4''$ diameter roll.

PIPING DRAWINGS

201. A piping drawing is started by laying out the center lines and locating the valves, fittings, etc., which can be shown more or less conventionally depending upon the scale. A complete treatment of the subject is given in "A Handbook on Piping," published by D. Van Nostrand Co., N. Y. Study Chap. X.

PROB. 141, Fig. 302.—From sketch, make a piping drawing to scale.

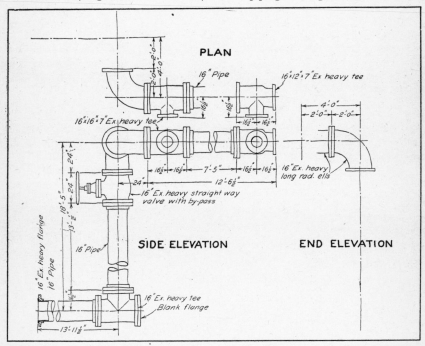

FIG. 302.   Prob. 141.   Piping Layout.

179

Fig. 303.—Make a drawing for a PIPE SUPPORT. These supports are made in sizes from 4″ to 72″ by the Pittsburgh Piping & Equipment Company. (11″ x 14″ working space.)

DIMENSIONS FOR PIPE SUPPORTS

	Size	Pipe													
		A	B	C	D	E	F	G	H	J	K	L	M	N	P
PROB. 142..	8	$8^3/_4$	3	4	$5^1/_4$	$^3/_4$	$^7/_8$	$2^1/_4$	$2^1/_4$	$1^3/_4$	$^5/_8$	$9^1/_4$	$1^1/_4$	24	$^1/_2$
PROB. 143..	24	$24^1/_4$	5	6	$7^5/_8$	$1^1/_4$	$1^3/_8$	6	$3^3/_4$	$2^1/_2$	1	$25^1/_8$	$1^3/_4$	$59^1/_2$	$^7/_8$
PROB. 144..	50	$50^1/_4$	8	9	11	$1^1/_2$	2	12	$5^1/_2$	$3^1/_2$	$1^3/_8$	$51^1/_2$	$2^1/_4$	118	$1^1/_4$

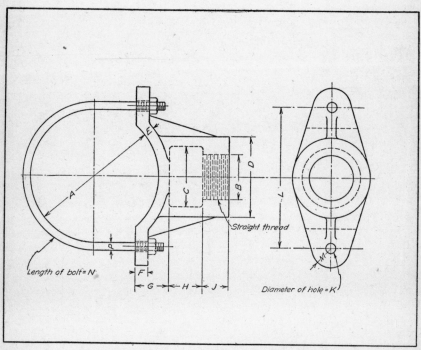

FIG. 303.   Probs. 142, 143 and 144.   Pipe Support.

Fig. 304.—Make a drawing for an iron body EXPANSION JOINT for 125 lbs. working pressure. The dimensions given in the table are from the Pittsburgh Piping & Equipment Co. (11″ x 14″ working space).

DIMENSIONS OF EXPANSION JOINTS

	Size	A	B	C	D	E	F	G	H	K	L	M	N	O	P	Q	No. Studs	Size Studs
PROB. 145. .	10	10 1/2	11 1/8	11 7/8	13	19 1/4	13 1/4	3	1 3/16	3/4	1 1/4	14 1/4	2	2 1/2	16	14 1/4	6 3/4	13/16
PROB. 146. .	12	12 5/8	13 1/4	14	15	21	14 5/8	3 1/4	1 1/4	13/16	1 1/4	16 1/2	2 1/8	2 5/8	19	17	6 3/4	13/16
PROB. 147. .	14	13 7/8	14 1/2	15 3/8	16 1/4	23 1/2	16 7/8	3 3/8	1 3/8	7/8	1 3/8	18	2 1/4	2 3/4	21	18 3/4	6 7/8	15/16

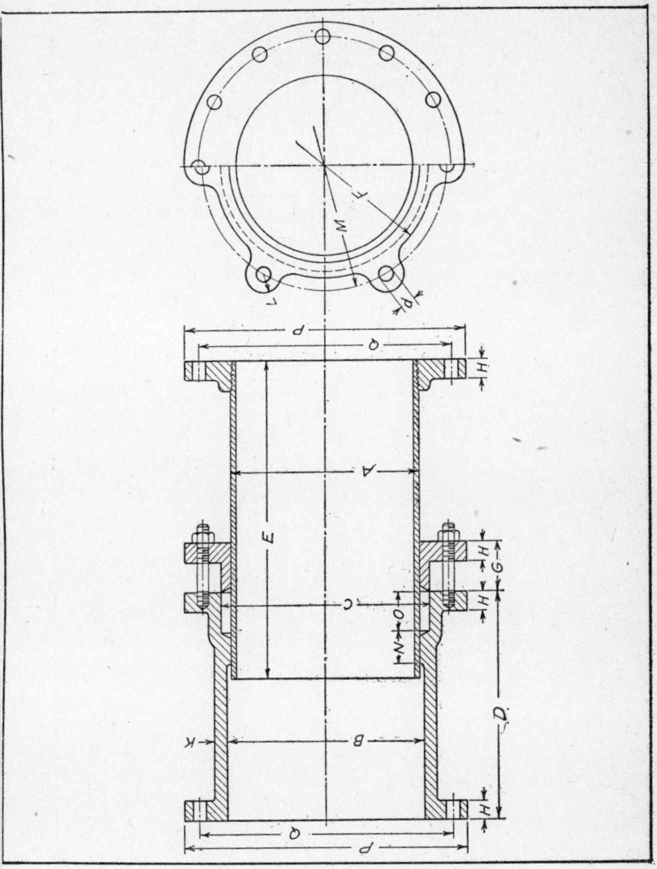

FIG. 304. Probs. 145, 146 and 147.

5″ x 6″ VERTICAL ENGINE

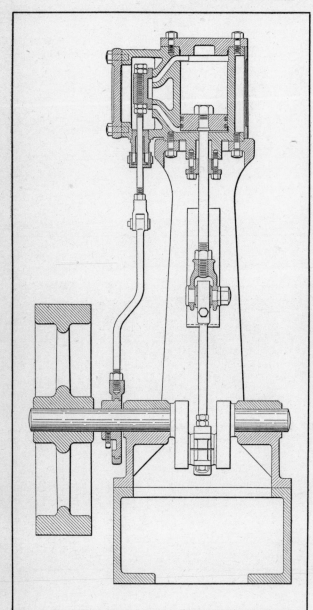

FIG. 305. Sectional Assembly.

202. The problems relating to Figures 305 to 322 comprise a set of drawings for a 5″ x 6″ vertical steam engine. They may be worked as separate problems or as a class problem. Each problem is stated by itself so they may be used in any way desired by the instructor. In some cases one figure refers to another for dimensions or information. This will require the student to check his drawing. A sectional assembly of the engine is shown in Fig. 305.

PROB. 148, Fig. 306.—From the sketch make a complete working drawing of the STEAM CHEST COVER. Give proper dimensions and indicate finished surfaces. Examine Figs. 305 and 319 to see where cover is used.

PROB. 149, Fig. 307.—From the sketch make a complete working drawing of the CYLINDER HEAD. Show one view in section. Examine Figs. 305 and 319 to see where head is used.

PROB. 150, Fig. 308.—From the sketch make a complete working drawing for the PISTON. Supply complete dimensions.

PROB. 151, Fig. 309.—Make a complete working drawing of the FLY WHEEL. Show one view in section.

PROB. 152, Fig. 310.—Make a complete working drawing of the BASE. Show front and side views as half sections.

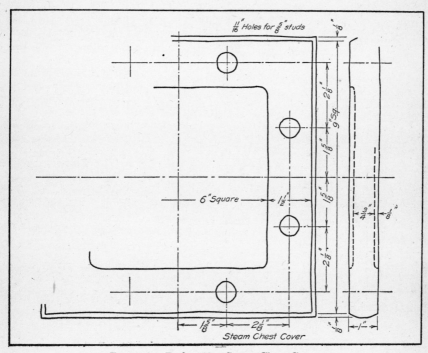

Fig. 306. Prob. 148. Steam Chest Cover.

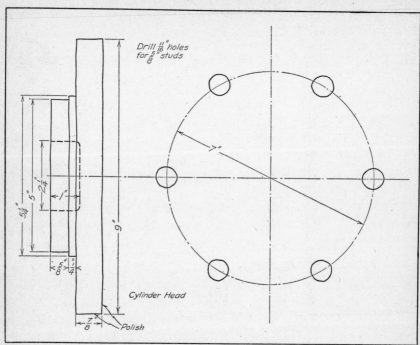

Drill $\frac{11}{16}"$ holes
for $\frac{5}{8}"$ studs

Cylinder Head

Polish

FIG. 307. Prob. 149. Cylinder Head.

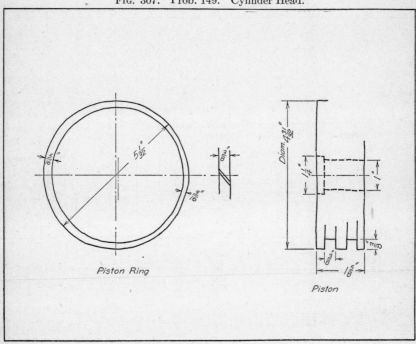

Piston Ring

Piston

FIG. 308. Prob. 150. Piston.

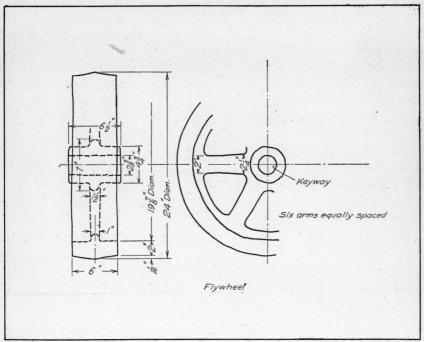

Fig. 309. Prob. 151. Flywheel.

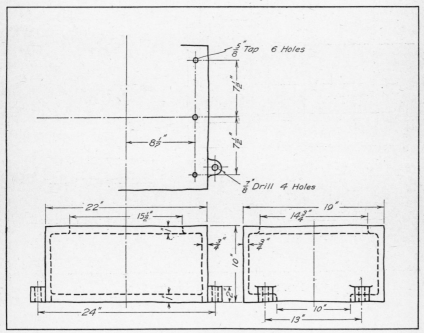

Fig. 310. Prob. 152. Base.

PROB. 153, Fig. 311.—Make a complete working drawing for the BEARING CAP. Show front and side views as half sections. Note babbitt and ¼″ oil pipe. Compare radii at *A*, *B*, and *C* with text and illustrations in Art. 121.

PROB. 154, Fig. 312.—Make a detail working drawing for the valve rod STUFFING BOX and piston rod GLAND.

PROB. 155, Fig. 313.—From the given sketch make an assembly drawing of the ECCENTRIC, with or without dimensions as directed by the instructor.

PROB. 156, Fig. 313.—From the given sketch make detail drawings of the eccentric sheave, eccentric straps, bolts and shim. Give all dimensions. Use two 11″ x 14″ sheets or one large sheet, Fig. 236.

PROB. 157, Fig. 314.—From the given sketch make a detail drawing of the valve and eccentric rods.

PROB. 158, Fig. 315.—From the sketch make a complete detail drawing of the CRANK SHAFT, PISTON ROD, etc.

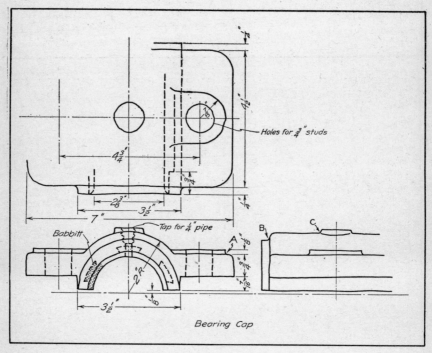

FIG. 311.　Prob. 153.　Bearing Cap.

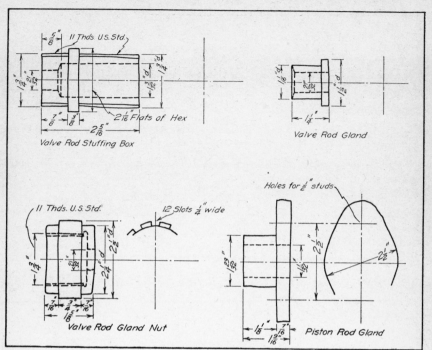

FIG. 312. Prob. 154. Stuffing Box Details.

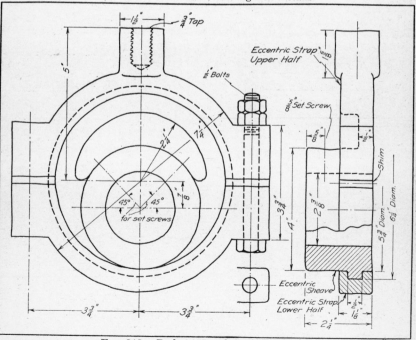

FIG. 313. Probs. 155 and 156. Eccentric.

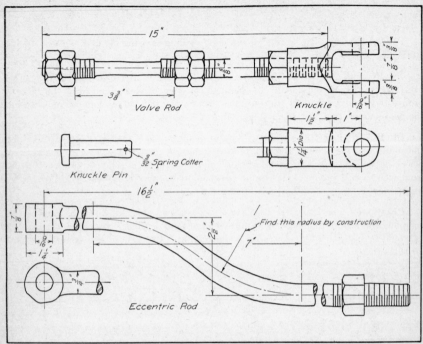

FIG. 314. Prob. 157. Eccentric Rod, etc.

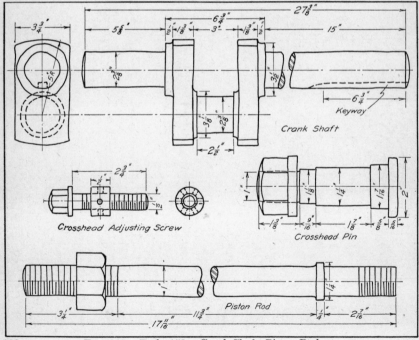

FIG. 315. Prob. 158. Crank Shaft, Piston Rod, etc.

PROB. 159, Fig. 316.—Make a complete working drawing of the CONNECTING ROD.

PROB. 160, Fig. 317.—Make a working drawing of the CONNECTING ROD DETAILS. Draw views as given, complete top view of wedge and draw top view of bronze box. Give complete dimensions. Obtain the bolt dimensions by reference to the places where they are used. Figs. 316 and 318.

PROB. 161, Fig. 318.—Make working drawing of the CRANK END BOXES for the connecting rod. Show the end views *with all full lines,* but *without all dotted lines.* Select dotted lines in all views carefully, omitting such as tend to confuse. Show front view in half section. Determine a few points in curve of intersection shown at *A* in top view.

PROB. 162, Figs. 316, 317, and 318.—Make a two view assembly drawing of the complete connecting rod, either with full views or part sections. Give such dimensions as would be necessary for machining or assembling. Use a large size sheet (Fig. 236) for this problem.

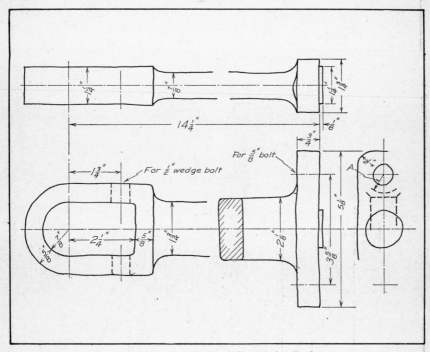

Fig. 316.   Prob. 159.   Connecting Rod.

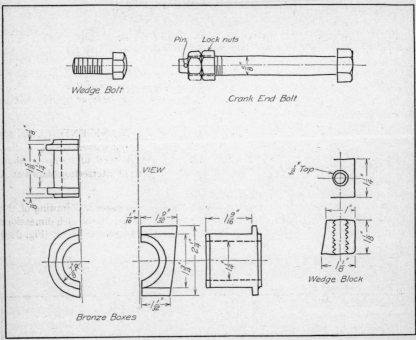

Fig. 317. Prob. 160. Connecting Rod Details.

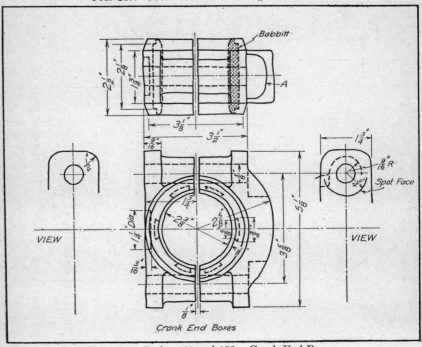

Crank End Boxes

Fig. 318. Probs. 161 and 162. Crank End Boxes.

PROB. 163, Fig. 319.—Make a working drawing of the STEAM CYLINDER showing the front view in section. Use regular sheet.

PROB. 164, Fig. 319.—Make a working drawing of the STEAM CYLINDER with following views. Front view as section on plane *A–A*; end view in full; complete top view in full; section on plane *B–B*. Use large sheet (Fig. 236).

PROB. 165, Fig. 320.—Make a working drawing of the CROSSHEAD SHOE. Show front view in section.

PROB. 166, Fig. 321.—Make a working drawing of the CROSSHEAD BODY. Show views given and two end views. Use judgment as to dotted lines on end views.

PROB. 167, Figs. 320 and 321.—Make an assembly drawing of the Crosshead and Shoe. Adjusting screw will be found on Fig. 315.

PROB. 168, Fig. 322.—Make a working drawing of the FRAME. Work out curves at *A* very carefully to give good appearance. Curves at *C* and *D* are to be found by projection and should be analyzed carefully. Show all views as half sections. Detail for Bearing Cap is given on Fig. 311.

PROB. 169.—Make a sectional assembly of the 5″ x 6″ Engine as shown in Fig. 305.

PROB. 170.—Make a sectional assembly of the 5″ x 6″ Engine taken through the vertical axis but at right angles to section shown in Fig. 305.

PROB. 171.—Make an exterior assembly of the 5″ x 6″ Engine, which will show the crosshead, connecting rod, etc.

PROB. 172.—Make an exterior assembly of the 5″ x 6″ Engine, which does not show the crosshead, connecting rod, etc.

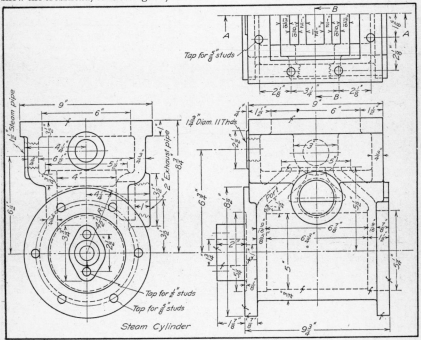

Fig. 319.   Probs. 163 and 164.   Steam Cylinder.

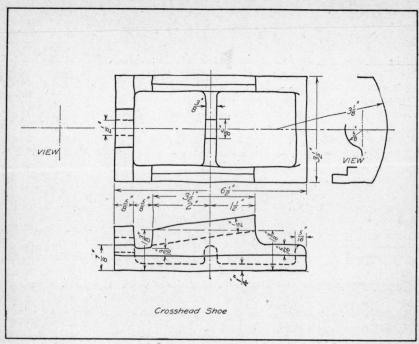

FIG. 320. Prob. 165. Crosshead Shoe.

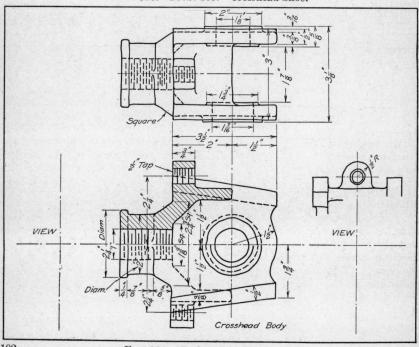

FIG. 321. Prob. 166. Crosshead.

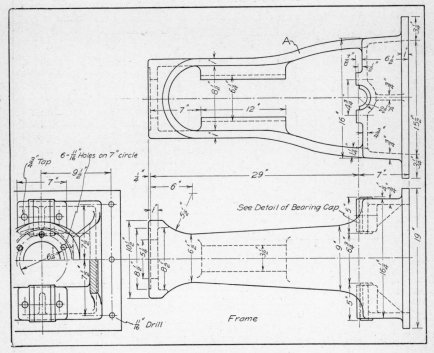

FIG. 322.   Prob. 168.   Frame.

ASSEMBLY AND DETAIL DRAWINGS

203. The drawings of a STEP BEARING, STEAM KETTLE, and PLUNGER PUMP are intended for reading problems as well as to give practice in applying the principles of drafting.   When assembling or detailing, check each piece with the parts with which it is used.

PROB. 173, Fig. 323.—Make detail working drawings for the parts of the STEP BEARING.   Scale $6'' = 1$ foot.   Use two regular sheets or one large sheet.

Consider the treatment of views, number of views, etc.   Do not copy the dimensions but finish the views and then locate dimensions without using the book.   Note that the bolt has a special head $\frac{1}{2}''$ thick and $1\frac{1}{2}''$ square.   On the right hand view one dimension line is shown incomplete to indicate that it is taken "about" the center.   This is done because the hollow space is not shown on both sides of the center line.

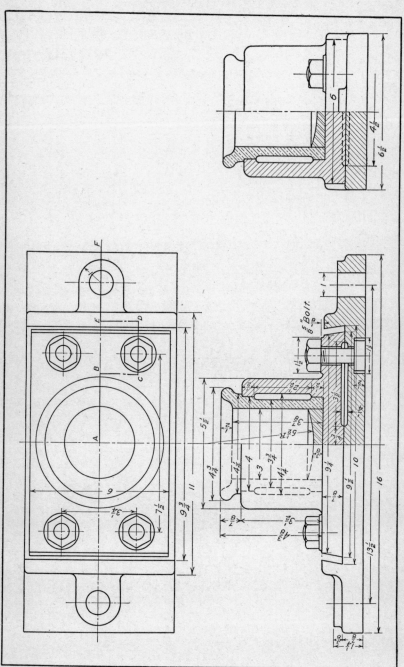

FIG. 323.   Prob. 173.   Step Bearing.

PROB. 174, Fig. 324.—Make detail working drawings of the STEAM KETTLE parts.

PROB. 175, Fig. 324.—Make an assembly working drawing of the STEAM JACK-ETED KETTLE. Draw sectional elevation or half section. Such dimensions as are not given are to be supplied by the student. The required bolts are to be drawn and specified. The bosses for the pipe may be about twice the outside diameter of the pipe.

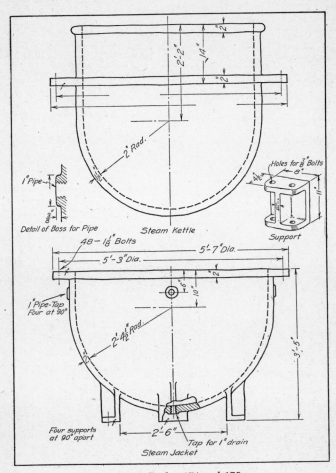

FIG. 324.   Probs. 174 and 175.

Completely dimension the drawing. The jacket is supported upon four supports, shown pictorially. The flange of the kettle rests upon the flange of the jacket and is bolted to it. Use large sheet. (Fig. 236.)

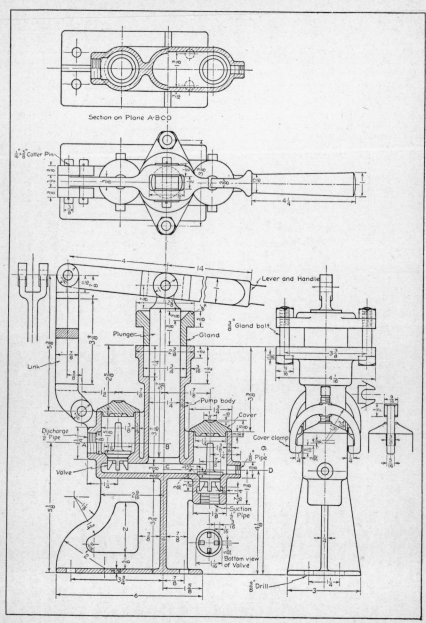

Fig. 325. Probs. 176, 177 and 178. Hand Pump.

PROB. 176, Fig. 325.—Make a detail working drawing of the PUMP BODY.

PROB. 177, Fig. 325.—Make a working drawing showing each detail separately for the $1^{1}/_{8}''$ plunger pump, for all parts except the pump body. Use large sheet.

PROB. 178, Fig. 325.—Make an exterior assembly drawing of the $1^{1}/_{8}''$ plunger pump. Give general dimensions only.

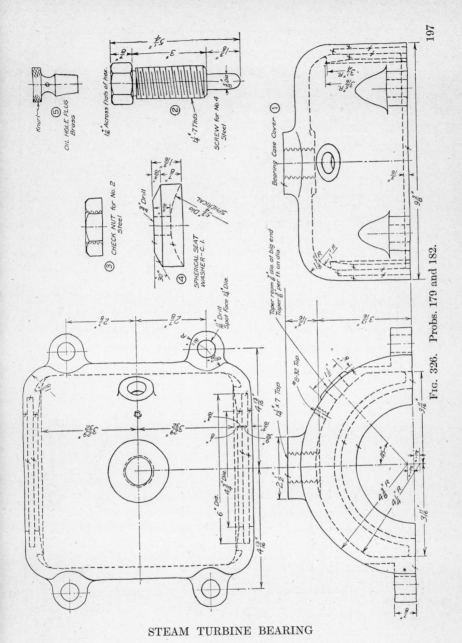

FIG. 326. Probs. 179 and 182.

STEAM TURBINE BEARING

204. The steam turbine bearing shown in Figs. 326, 327, and 328 is for a Type 6, B. F. Sturtevant Steam Turbine. The bearings are split to permit easy adjustment. The two halves are held together with cap screws. The spherical seating makes the bearing self-aligning. The rapidly revolving oiling ring takes oil from the oil pocket and deposits it on the shaft where it is distributed by the oil grooves in the bearings.

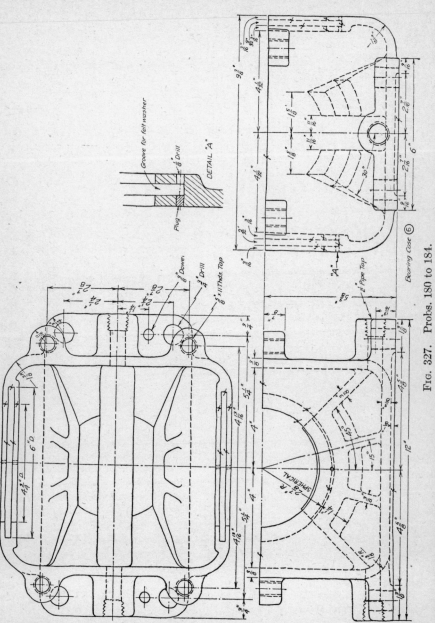

FIG. 327. Probs. 180 to 184.

An idea of the assembly may be had by reference to Fig. 73. The adjusting screw (Part No. 2, Fig. 326) is used to screw through the bearing casing cover, causing the spherical seat (Part No. 4, Fig. 326) to grip the linings (Part No. 7, Fig. 328). The lock nut (Part No. 3, Fig. 326) is used to hold the adjusting screw in position.

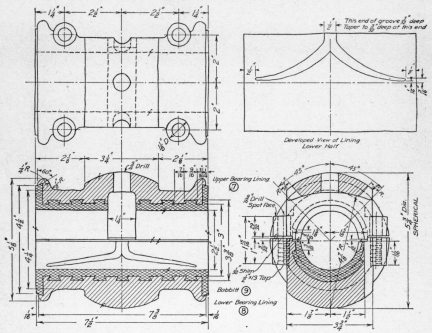

FIG. 328. Probs. 181 to 184.

The list of parts is as follows:

1. Bearing Case Cover, Fig. 326.
2. Adjusting Screw, Fig. 326.
3. Check Nut, Fig. 326.
4. Spherical Seat, Fig. 326.
5. Oil Hole Plug, Fig. 326.
   Safety Chain for Plug, not shown.
   No. 8—32 Machine Screw $^1/_2''$ long
   to hold chain, not shown.
6. Bearing Case, Fig. 327.

$^1/_2''$ Pipe Plugs, not shown.
Felt Washers, not shown.
$^3/_8''$ Dowel Pins, 2″ long, not shown.
$^5/_8''$ Studs, $2^7/_{16}''$ long, not shown.
7. Upper Bearing Lining, Fig. 328.
8. Lower Bearing Lining, Fig. 328.
9. Phoenix Metal, Fig. 328.
   $^1/_2''$—13 Cap Screws, not shown.
   Oil Ring $5^1/_2''$ inside diameter, $6^1/_4''$
   outside diameter.

PROB. 179, Fig. 326.—Make a detail drawing of the BEARING CASE COVER. Show the front and side views as half sections.

PROB. 180, Fig. 327.—Make a detail drawing of the BEARING CASE. Show the front and side views as half sections.

PROB. 181, Fig. 328.—Make a detail drawing of the BEARING LINING. Will go full size on large size sheet, Fig. 236. Draw front view as a half section.

PROB. 182, Figs. 326, 327, and 328.—Make an exterior assembly drawing of the complete bearing. Show two or three views as specified by instructor.

PROB. 183.—Make an assembly drawing of the complete bearing showing a section through the axis. One view only.

PROB. 184.—Make an assembly drawing of the complete bearing, showing a section at right angles to the axis. One view only.

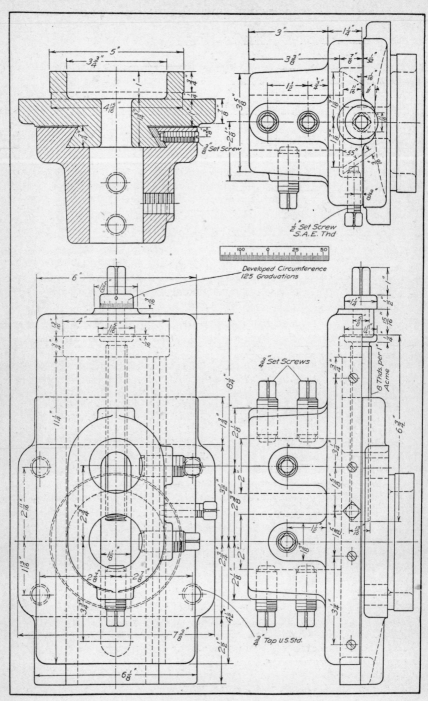

Fig. 329. Prob. 185.

SLIDE TOOL HOLDER

205. The slide tool holder shown in Fig. 329 is from a drawing supplied by the Foster Machine Company, Elkhart, Ind., and is described by them as follows:

"Designed for boring, recessing, back facing, and like operations, this tool combines a high degree of rigidity with adaptability. The cutters can be carried in either of two holes. Wear on the slide of the tool can be taken up by means of a gib. The tool adjusting screw carries a graduated dial which feature aids materially in setting the tool. The slide tool is used on Foster turret lathes."

PROB. 185.—Make detail working drawings of each part of the vertical slide tool. Consider choice of views, treatment of views, scale, etc., very carefully. If drawn full size larger sheets than specified in Fig. 236 will be required.

POWER PUNCHING PRESS

206. The "Stiles" Punching Press, No. 2—B shown in Fig. 330 is built by the E. W. Bliss Company, Brooklyn, N. Y., who furnished drawings from which the following figures were made. This type of press is made in three sizes, either as flywheel or geared presses. Larger sheets than specified in Fig. 236 will be required. About 18″ x 24″ working space for a minimum if drawn to a scale of 3″ = 1 ft.

207. The "Stiles" clutch is illustrated in partial assembly in Fig. 335. Views are shown in direction of arrows "A" and "B" from the plane indicated. The clutch collar is keyed to the shaft.

The dog holds the wheel pin in place. When the treadle is depressed one cam on the clutch fork releases the wheel pin allowing it to engage a recess in the clutch collar and revolve the shaft. When the treadle is released the wheel pin is pushed back into the wheel by a wedge cam on the clutch fork and is held by the dog. Three wheel pins are used on the flywheel of this press.

PROB. 186, Fig. 331.—Make a working drawing of the FRAME. Show top view in full and necessary sections. Do not simply copy the sketch but consider treatment of views.

PROB. 187.—Make detail drawings of the separate parts as directed by your instructor. It will be necessary to study the complete machine in order to check the parts. Use small or large standard sheets, Fig. 234 or Fig. 236. Several sheets will be required. Plan the arrangement of parts and treatment of views.

PROB. 188.—Make an assembly drawing of the complete press. Show all parts in their working positions. Section such parts as are necessary to show the construction clearly. Choose scale and plan views for instructor's criticism. Work carefully to check details. Drawing must be accurate. Do not dimension. Study clutch as given on details and in Fig. 335.

PROB. 189.—Make an exterior or full view assembly drawing of the press. Do not show hidden surfaces. Give set-up and space dimensions only.

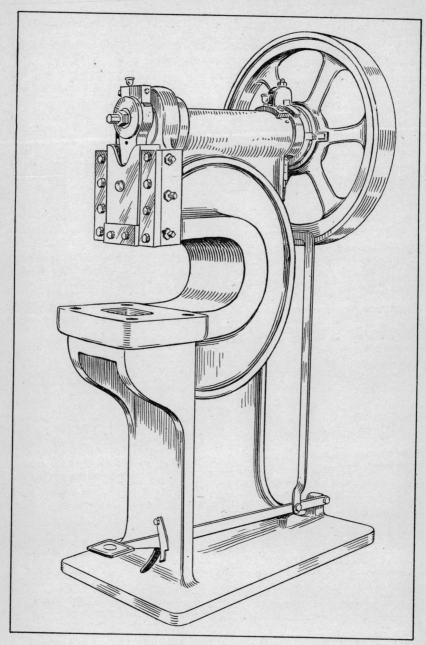

FIG. 330. Press.

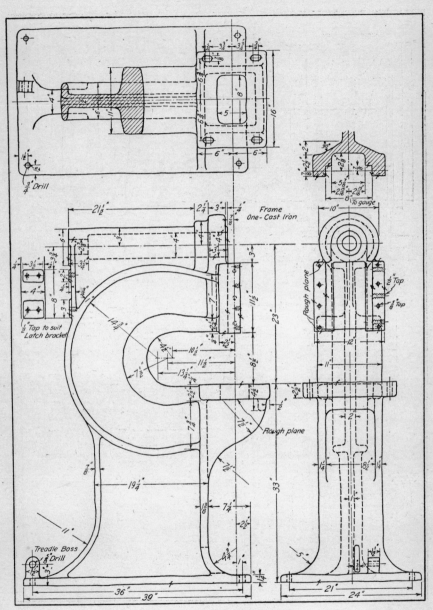

Fig. 331. Probs. 186 to 189.

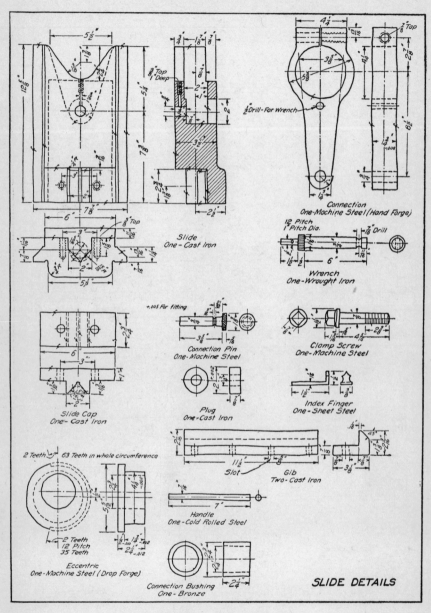

SLIDE DETAILS

Fig. 332.   Probs. 187, 188 and 189.

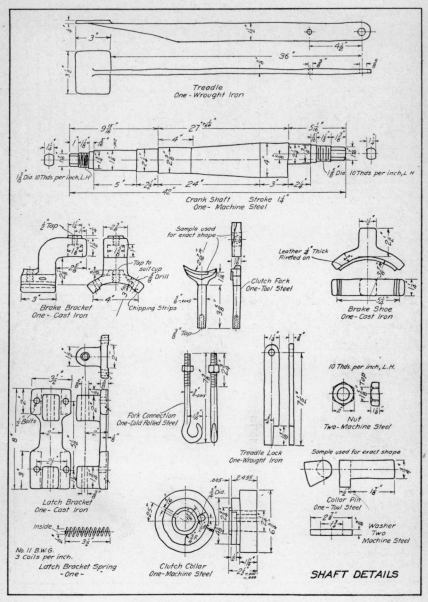

Fig. 333. Probs. 187, 188 and 189.

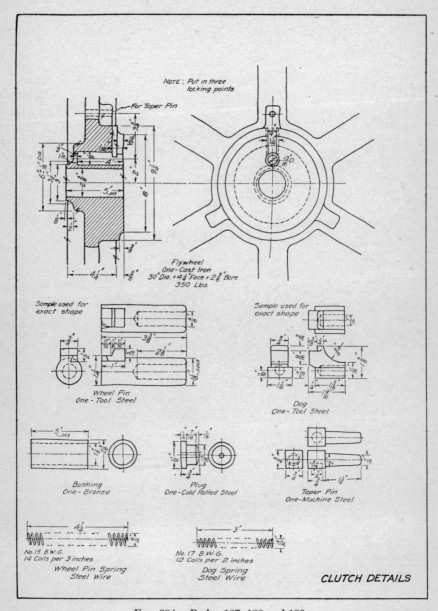

CLUTCH DETAILS

Fig. 334. Probs. 187, 188 and 189.

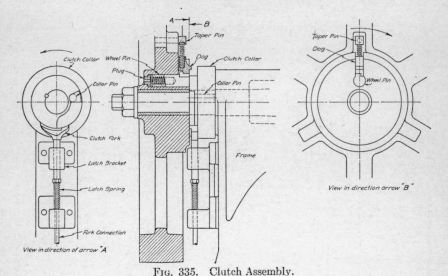

Fɪɢ. 335. Clutch Assembly.

AMMONIA PUMP END

208. A pump for ammonia must be constructed entirely of iron or steel. The operation of the water end of an ordinary reciprocating pump should be understood before starting this problem. Fig. 336 shows an ammonia pump cylinder and Fig. 337 some suggested details. If possible it would be well for the student to refer to "Pumping Machinery" by A. M. Greene. Choose scales for details carefully, either full size or half size depending upon the piece.

PROB. 190.—Fig. 336.—Make a detail working drawing of the ammonia PUMP CYLINDER. Show top view in full, front view as a half section on planes indicated, a cross section, and a full end view. Large sheet, Fig. 236.

PROB. 191, Fig. 337.—Make a working drawing of the AIR CHAMBER. (11" x 14" space.)

PROB. 192, Fig. 337.—Make a working drawing of the valves, valve seats, and plugs. The sketches are suggestive. Wing valves are shown but ball valves may be used with advice of the instructor. A partial assembly showing the valves in place may be necessary in order to determine dimensions. It should be possible to remove the suction valve without taking out the discharge valve seat. The lift of a valve to give full opening is one fourth the diameter but the practical lift is about one half this amount. Use 11" x 14" space.

PROB. 193, Fig. 337.—Make a working drawing of the PISTON. (11" x 14" space.) Sketch is suggestive only.

PROB. 194, Fig. 337.—Make a working drawing of the outside CYLINDER HEAD. Consider method of making joint (11" x 14" space).

PROB. 195, Fig. 338.—Make a working drawing of the inside CYLINDER HEAD and double stuffing box. Note the opening from between the two packing spaces which connects with the suction chamber of the pump cylinder. The three tie rods hold the pump cylinder and steam cylinder in alignment. The steam cylinder is not part of our problem. (11" x 14" space.)

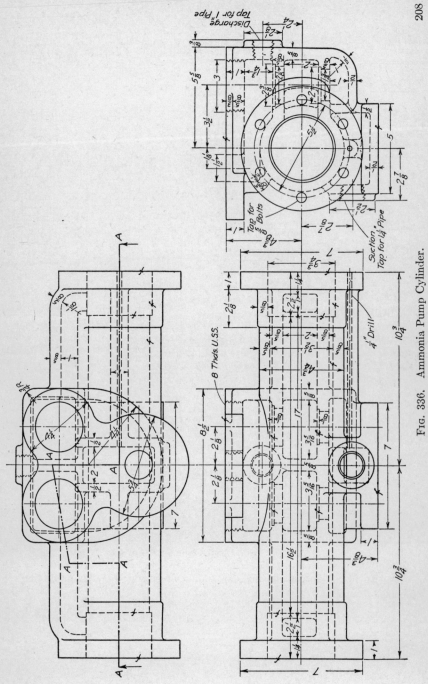

FIG. 336. Ammonia Pump Cylinder.

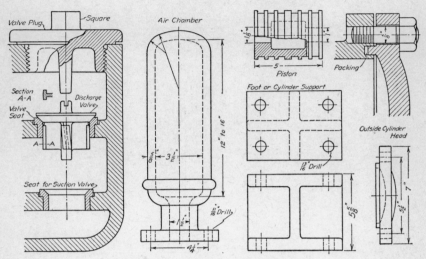

Fig. 337. Ammonia Pump Details.

PROB. 196, Fig. 337.—Make a working drawing of the FOOT or support. (11″ x 14″ space.)

PROB. 197, Figs. 336, 337, and 338.—Make an assembly drawing of the ammonia pump end. Show two sectional views with all parts in working positions. Use cutting planes which are shown on the pump cylinder drawing. This will require a special size large sheet.

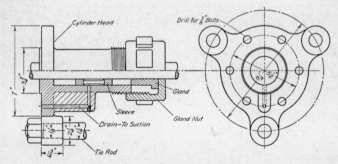

Fig. 338. Inside Cylinder Head.

PROB. 198, Figs. 336, 337, and 338.—Make an exterior assembly drawing of the ammonia pump end.

INDEX

D. VAN NOSTRAND COMPANY

8 WARREN STREET

NEW YORK

SHORT-TITLE CATALOG

OF

𝕻𝖚𝖇𝖑𝖎𝖈𝖆𝖙𝖎𝖔𝖓𝖘 𝖆𝖓𝖉 𝕴𝖒𝖕𝖔𝖗𝖙𝖆𝖙𝖎𝖔𝖓𝖘

OF

SCIENTIFIC AND ENGINEERING BOOKS

This list includes
the technical publications of the following English publishers:

SCOTT, GREENWOOD & CO.   JAMES MUNRO & CO., Ltd.
CONSTABLE & COMPANY, Ltd.   TECHNICAL PUBLISHING CO.
BENN BROTHERS, Ltd.

for whom D. Van Nostrand Company are American agents.

AUGUST, 1921

SHORT=TITLE CATALOG

OF THE

Publications and Importations

OF

D. VAN NOSTRAND COMPANY

8 WARREN ST., N. Y.

All Prices in this list are NET.
All bindings are in cloth unless otherwise noted.
Prices subject to change without notice.

Arnold, E.   Armature Windings of Direct-Current Dynamos......8vo, 2 00
Asch, W., and Asch, D.   The Silicates in Chemistry and Commerce.8vo, 7 50
Ashe, S. W., and Keiley, J. D.   Electric Railways. Theoretically and
    Practically Treated.   Vol. I. Rolling Stock..............12mo, *2 50
Ashe, S. W.   Electric Railways.   Vol. II. Engineering Preliminaries and
    Direct Current Sub-Stations.........................12mo, *2 50
—— Electricity: Experimentally and Practically Applied..........12mo, *2 00
Ashley, R. H.   Chemical Calculations......................12mo, 2 50
Atkins, W.   Common Battery Telephony Simplified..............12mo, *1 25
Atkinson, A. A.   Electrical and Magnetic Calculations............8vo, *1 50
Atkinson, J. J.   Friction of Air in Mines......................16mo, 0 75
Atkinson, J. J., and Williams, Jr., E. H.   Gases Met with in Coal Mines.
    16mo, 0 75
Atkinson, P.   The Elements of Electric Lighting..............12mo, 1 50
—— The Elements of Dynamic Electricity and Magnetism........12mo, 2 00
Auchincloss, W. S.   Link and Valve Motions Simplified........8vo, 2 00
Audley J. A.   Silica and the Silicates...........................8vo, 4 50
Austin, E.   Single Phase Electric Railways....................4to, *5 00
Austin and Cohn.   Pocketbook of Radiotelegraphy..........(In Press.)
Ayrton, H.   The Electric Arc.................................8vo, 5 50

Baff, W. E.   Sale of Inventions.............................12mo, 2 00
Baker, A. L.   Quaternions....................................8vo, 1 50
—— Thick-Lens Optics..12mo, 2 00
Baker, Benj.   Pressure of Earthwork........................16mo,
Baker, G. S.   Ship Form, Resistance and Screw Propulsion......8vo, *4 50
Baker, I. O.   Levelling..16mo, 0 75
Baker, M. N.   Potable Water.................................16mo, 0 75
—— Sewerage and Sewage Purification......................16mo, 0 75
Baker, T. T.   Telegraphic Transmission of Photographs........12mo,
    (Reprinting.)
Bale, G. R.   Modern Iron Foundry Practice.   12mo.
    Vol. I.   Foundry Equipment, Materials Used................... *3 00
Ball, J. W.   Concrete Structures in Railways.................8vo, *2 50
Ball, R. S.   Popular Guide to the Heavens....................8vo, 7 50
—— Natural Sources of Power................................8vo, 2 50
Ball, W. V.   Law Affecting Engineers.........................8vo, *3 50
Bankson, Lloyd.   Slide Valve Diagrams......................16mo, 0 75
Barham, G. B.   Development of the Incandescent Electric Lamp..8vo, 2 50
Barker, A. F.   Textiles and Their Manufacture................8vo, 4 00
Barker, A. F., and Midgley, E.   Analysis of Woven Fabrics......8vo, 3 50
Barker, A. H.   Graphic Methods of Engine Design.............12mo, 2 00
—— Heating and Ventilation.................................4to, 9 00
Barnard, J. H.   The Naval Militiaman's Guide..........16mo, leather 1 00
Barnard, Major J. G.   Rotary Motion.......................16mo, 0 75
Barnes, J. B.   Elements of Military Sketching..............16mo. *0 75
Barnett, E. deB.   Coal-Tar Dyes and Intermediates............8vo, 3 50
—— Explosives 8vo, 5 00
—— Synthetic Dyes..............................8vo (In Press.)
—— Anthracene and Anthraquinone............................8vo, 6 00
Barrowcliffe, M., and Carr, F. H.   Organic Medical Chemicals..8vo, 4 00

Barrus, G. H. Engine Tests.................................8vo,   *4 00
Baterden, J. R. Timber....................................8vo,   *2 50
Bates, E. L., and Charlesworth, F. Practical Mathematics and
    Geometry..12mo,
    Part I. Preliminary Course...........................   1 00
    Part II. Elementary Course............................   1 00
    Part III. Advanced Course..............................   1 50
—— Practical Mathematics..................................12mo,   *2 00
—— Practical Geometry and Graphics.......................12mo,   2 00
Batey, J. The Science of Works Management..............12mo,   *2 00
—— Steam Boilers and Combustion..........................12mo,   *2 00
Bayonet Training Manual...................................16mo,   0 30
Beadle, C. Chapters on Papermaking. Five Volumes....12mo, each,   2 50
Beaumont, R. Color in Woven Design.....................8vo,   *6 00
—— Finishing of Textile Fabrics...........................8vo,   *5 00
—— Standard Cloths 8vo,   *6 00
—— Woollen and Worsted..................................8vo,   10 00
Beaumont, W. W. The Steam-Engine Indicator.............8vo,   2 50
Bechhold, H. Colloids in Biology and Medicine..............8vo,   5 00
Beckwith, A. Pottery..............................8vo, paper,   0 60
Bedell, F. The Airplane.................................8vo,   3 00
Bedell, F., and Pierce, C. A. Direct and Alternating Current Manual.
                                                                   8vo,   2 50
Beech, F. Dyeing of Cotton Fabrics......................8vo,   5 00
—— Dyeing of Woolen Fabrics...............................8vo,   *3 50
Beggs, G. E. Stresses in Railway Girders and Bridges.....(*In Press.*)
Begtrup, J. The Slide Valve..............................8vo,   *2 00
Bender, C. E. Continuous Bridges........................16mo,   0 75
—— Proportions of Pins Used in Bridges....................16mo,   0 75
Bengough, G. D. Brass...............................(*In Press.*)
Bennett, H. G. The Manufacture of Leather................8vo,   6 00
—— Animal Proteids......................8vo, (*In Press.*)
Bernthsen, A. A Text-book of Organic Chemistry.............12mo,   3 50
Bersch, J. The Manufacture of Earth Colors...............12mo,   3 00
Beveridge, J. Papermaker's Pocket Book...................12mo,   *4 00
Binnie, Sir A. Rainfall Reservoirs and Water Supply.........8vo,   4 00
Binns, C. F. Manual of Practical Potting.....................8vo,   8 00
—— The Potter's Craft.......................12mo,   *2 00
Birchmore, W. H. Interpretation of Gas Analysis............12mo,   *1 25
Blake, E. H. Drainage and Sanitation.......................8vo,   6 00
Blaine, R. G. The Calculus and Its Applications...............12mo,   *1 75
Blanchard, W. M. Laboratory Exercises in General Chemistry..12mo,   1 00
Blasdale, W. C. Quantitative Chemical Analysis..............12mo,   3 00
Bloch, L. Science of Illumination............................8vo,   2 50
Blyth, A. W. Foods: Their Composition and Analysis..........8vo,   12 00
—— Poisons: Their Effects and Detection.....................8vo,   8 50
Böckmann, F. Celluloid.....................................12mo,   *2 50
Bodmer, G. R. Hydraulic Motors and Turbines................12mo,   6 00
Boileau, J. T. Traverse Tables.............................8vo,   5 00

Buel, R. H.   Safety Valves.................................16mo,   o 75
Bunkley, J. W.   Military and Naval Recognition Book.........16mo,   1 00
Burley, G. W.   Lathes.   Their Construction and Operation.....12mo,   2 00
—— Machine and Fitting Shop Practice. 2 vols.........12mo, each,   2 00
—— Testing of Machine Tools.................................12mo,   2 00
Burnside, W.   Bridge Foundations...........................12mo,   *2 00
Burstall, F. W.   Energy Diagram for Gas.   With Text...........8vo,   1 50
—— Diagram.   Sold separately.................................   *1 00
Burt, W. A.   Key to the Solar Compass.................16mo, leather,   2 50
Buskett, E. W.   Fire Assaying...............................12mo,   *1 25
Butler, H. J.   Motor Bodies and Chassis.......................8vo,   *3 00
Byers, H. G., and Knight, H. G.   Notes on Qualitative Analysis....8vo,
                                 (*New Edition in Preparation.*)

Cain, W.   Brief Course in the Calculus.......................12mo,   *1 75
—— Elastic Arches ....16mo,   o 75
—— Maximum Stresses ....16mo,   o 75
—— Practical Designing Retaining of Walls.................16mo,   o 75
—— Theory of Steel-concrete Arches and of Vaulted Structures.
                                                        16mo,   o 75
—— Theory of Voussoir Arches...............................16mo,   o 75
—— Symbolic Algebra ....16mo,   o 75
Calvert, G. T.   The Manufacture of Sulphate of Ammonia and
      Crude Ammonia 12mo,   4 00
Camm, S.   Aeroplane Construction............................12mo,   3 00
Carhart, H. S.   Thermo Electromotive Force in Electric Cells...12mo,   2 00
Carey, A. E., and Oliver, F. W.   Tidal Lands.................8vo,   5 00
Carpenter, F. D.   Geographical Surveying....................16mo,
Carpenter, R. C., and Diederichs, H.   Internal Combustion Engines.8vo,   5 50
Carpmael, H.   Electric Welding and Welding Appliances........4to,   5 00
Carter, H. A.   Ramie (Rhea), China Grass....................12mo,   *3 00
Carter, H. R.   Modern Flax, Hemp, and Jute Spinning..........8vo,   *3 50
—— Bleaching, Dyeing and Finishing of Fabrics...............8vo,   *1 25
Cary, E. R.   Solution of Railroad Problems with the Slide Rule.16mo,   1 25
Casler, M. D.   Simplified Reinforced Concrete Mathematics....12mo,   1 25
Cathcart, W. L.   Machine Design.   Part I. Fastenings...........8vo,   *3 00
Cathcart, W. L., and Chaffee, J. I.   Elements of Graphic Statics...8vo,   *3 00
—— Short Course in Graphics.................................12mo,   1 50
Caven, R. M.   The Foundations of Chemical Theory.............8vo,   4 00
Caven, R. M., and Lander, G. D.   Systematic Inorganic Chemistry.12mo,   2 25
Chalkley, A. P.   Diesel Engines................................8vo,   5 00
Chalmers, T. W.   The Production and Treatment of Vegetable Oils,
                                                        4to,   7 50
—— Paper Making and its Machinery..........................4to,   8 00
—— The Gyroscopic Compass.................................8vo   4 00
Chambers' Mathematical Tables.............................8vo,   2 50
Chambers, G. F.   Astronomy...................16mo (*Reprinting.*)
Chappel, E.   Five Figure Mathematical Tables................8vo,   2 50
Charnock, Mechanical Technology.............................8vo,   3 50
Charpentier, P.   Timber.......................................8vo,   *6 00
Chatley, H.   Principles and Designs of Aeroplanes.............16mo,   o 75
—— How to Use Water Power.................................12mo,   *1 50
—— Gyrostatic Balancing 8vo,   *1 25

Crehore, A. C.   Mystery of Matter and Energy.................8vo,   1 00
—— The Atom...12mo,   2 00
Crocker, F. B., and Arendt, M.   Electric Motors..............8vo,   2 00
Crocker, F. B., and Wheeler, S. S.   The Management of Electrical Machinery..12mo,   *1 00
Crosby, E. U., Fiske, H. A., and Forster, H. W.   Handbook of Fire Protection..12mo,   4 00
Cross, C. F., Bevan, E. J., and Sindall, R. W.   Wood Pulp and Its Uses..8vo,   3 50
Crosskey, L. R.   Elementary Perspective......................8vo,   1 50
Crosskey, L. R., and Thaw, J.   Advanced Perspective...........8vo,   2 00
Culley, J. L.   Theory of Arches..............................16mo,   0 75
Cushing, H. C., Jr., and Harrison, N.   Central Station Management...   *2 00

Dadourian, H. M.   Analytical Mechanics......................12mo,   3 75
——Graphic Statics..8vo,   0 75
Danby, A.   Natural Rock Asphalts and Bitumens.............8vo,   *2 50
Darling, E. R.   Inorganic Chemical Synonyms...............12mo,   1 00
Davenport, C.   The Book...................................8vo,   2 50
Davey, N.   The Gas Turbine...............................8vo,   *4 00
Davies, F. H.   Electric Power and Traction.................8vo,   *2 00
Davis, A. M.   Introduction to Palaeontology................8vo,   3 50
—— Foundations and Machinery Fixing.......................16mo,   1 00
Deerr, N.   Sugar Cane........................8vo (Reprinting.)
Deite, C.   Manual of Toilet Soap-Making....................8vo,   7 50
De la Coux, H.   The Industrial Uses of Water.................8vo,   5 00
Del Mar, W. A.   Electric Power Conductors.................8vo,   *2 00
Denny, G. A.   Deep-level Mines of the Rand................4to,   *10 00
De Roos, J. D. C.   Linkages................................16mo,   0 75
Derr, W. L.   Block Signal Operation...............Oblong 12mo,   *1 50
Desaint, A.   Three Hundred Shades and How to Mix Them.....8vo,   *9 00
De Varona, A.   Sewer Gases................................16mo,   0 75
Devey, R. G.   Mill and Factory Wiring.....................12mo,   1 00
Dichmann, Carl.   Basic Open-Hearth Steel Process...........12mo,   4 00
Dieterich, K.   Analysis of Resins, Balsams, and Gum Resins....8vo,   7 00
Dilworth, E. C.   Steel Railway Bridges.....................4to,   6 00
Dinger, Lieut. H. C.   Care and Operation of Naval Machinery...12mo,   *3 00
Dixon, D. B.   Machinist's and Steam Engineer's Practical Calculator.
16mo, morocco,   1 25
Dommett, W. E.   Motor Car Mechanism.....................12mo,   *2 00
Dorr, B. F.   The Surveyor's Guide and Pocket Table-book.
16mo, morocco,   2 00
Draper, C. H.   Heat and the Principles of Thermo-Dynamics..12mo,   2 25
Draper, E. G.   Navigating the Ship........................12mo,   2 00
Dubbel, H.   High Power Gas Engines.......................8vo,   *5 00
Dumbleton, J. E.   Aerial Navigation.........................12mo,   4 00
Dumesny, P., and Noyer, J.   Wood Products, Distillates, and Extracts.
8vo,   *5 00
Duncan, W. G., and Penman, D.   The Electrical Equipment of Collieries.
8vo,   *5 00
Dunkley, W. G.   Design of Machine Elements.   Two volumes..8vo,each,   2 00
Dunstan, A. E., and Thole, F. B. T.   Textbook of Practical Chemistry.
12mo,   3 00

Durham, H. W.   Saws..8vo,   2 50

Duthie, A. L.   Decorative Glass Processes.......................8vo,   2 50

Dwight, H. B.   Transmission Line Formulas...................8vo,   *2 00

Dyke, A. L.   Dyke's Automobile and Gasoline Engine Encyclopedia,
8vo,   6 00

Dyson, S. S.   A Manual of Chemical Plant.   12 parts....4to, paper,   7 50

Dyson, S. S., and Clarkson, S. S.   Chemical Works............8vo,   *9 00

Eccles, W. H.   Wireless Telegraphy and Telephony............12mo,   7 00

Eck, J.   Light, Radiation and Illumination......................8vo,   2 50

Eddy, L. C.   Laboratory Manual of Alternating Currents.......12mo,   0 50

Edelman, P.   Inventions and Patents.........................12mo,   2 00

Edgcumbe, K.   Industrial Electrical Measuring Instruments.. ...8vo,   5 00

Edler, R.   Switches and Switchgear............................8vo,   3 50

Eissler, M.   The Metallurgy of Gold............................8vo,   9 00

—— The Metallurgy of Silver................................8vo,   4 00

—— The Metallurgy of Argentiferous Lead....................8vo,   6 25

Ekin, T. C.   Water Pipe and Sewage Discharge Diagrams ....folio,   *3 00

Electric Light Carbons, Manufacture of.........................8vo,   1 00

Eliot, C. W., and Storer, F. H.   Compendious Manual of Qualitative
Chemical Analysis....................................12mo,   1 50

Eliott, A. W. M.   Rectangular Areas.........................12mo,   3 00

Ellis, C.   Hydrogenation of Oils..............................8vo,   7 50

—— Ultraviolet Light, Its Applications in Chemical Arts.....12mo,
(In Press)

—— and Meigs, J. V.   Gasoline and Other Motor Fuels.........8vo,   10 00

Ellis, G.   Modern Technical Drawing...........................8vo,   *2 00

—— Modern Practical Carpentry..................................4to,   7 50

Ennis, Wm. D.   Linseed Oil and Other Seed Oils...............8vo,   5 00

—— Applied Thermodynamics....................................8vo,   5 00

—— Vapors for Heat Engines.................................12mo,   *1 00

Ermen, W. F. A.   Materials Used in Sizing 8vo,   *2 00

Erwin, M.   The Universe and the Atom..........12mo (Reprinting.)

Ewing, A. J.   Magnetic Induction in Iron....................8vo,   5 00

Faber, O.   Ferraris Dioptric Instruments......................8vo,   3 00

Fage, A.   Airscrews in Theory and Practice..................4to,   10 00

Fairchild, J. F.   Graphical Compass Conversion Chart and Tables...   0 50

Fairie, J.   Notes on Lead Ores...............................12mo,   *0 50

—— Notes on Pottery Clays.....................................12mo,   *2 00

Fairley, W., and Andre, Geo. J.   Ventilation of Coal Mines....16mo,   0 75

Fairweather, W. C.   Foreign and Colonial Patent Laws...........8vo,   *3 00

Falk, K. G.   Chemical Reactions: Their Supply and Mechanism..12mo,   2 50

Fanning, J. T.   Hydraulic and Water-supply Engineering.........8vo,   *5 00

Farnsworth, P. V.   Shop Mathematics...   ......12mo (In Press.)

Fay, I. W.   The Coal-tar Dyes................................8vo,   5 00

Fernbach, R. L.   Glue and Gelatine............................8vo,   *3 00

Findlay, A.   The Treasures of Coal Tar.......................12mo,   1 25

Firth, J. B.   Practical Physical Chemistry....................12mo,   1 25

Fischer, E.   The Preparation of Organic Compounds...........12mo,   2 00

Fisher, H. K. C., and Darby, W. C.   Submarine Cable Testing...8vo,   4 00

Fleischmann, W.   The Book of the Dairy.........8vo (Reprinting.)

Fleming, J. A.   The Alternate-current Transformer.   Two Volumes. 8vo
Vol. I.   The Induction of Electric Currents...................... *6 50
Vol, II.   The Utilization of Induced Currents................... 6 50
—— Propagation of Electric Currents...........................8vo,   3 75
—— A Handbook for the Electrical Laboratory and Testing Room.   Two
Volumes.......................................8vo, each,   *6 50
Fleury, P.   Preparation and Uses of White Zinc Paints.........8vo,   3 00
Flynn, P. J.   Flow of Water.................................12mo,   0 75
—— Hydraulic Tables 16mo,   0 75
Foster, H. A.   Electrical Engineers' Pocket-book.   (Seventh Edition.)
12mo, leather,   5 00
—— Engineering Valuation of Public Utilities and Factories.......8vo,   *3 00
Fowle, F. F.   Overhead Transmission Line Crossings...........12mo,   *1 50
—— The Solution of Alternating Current Problems.....8vo (In Press.)
Fox, W. G.   Transition Curves................................16mo,   0 75
Fox, W., and Thomas, C. W.   Practical Course in Mechanical Draw-
ing..12mo,   1 25
Foye, J. C.   Chemical Problems.............................16mo,   0 75
—— Handbook of Mineralogy................................16mo,   0 75
Francis, J. B.   Lowell Hydraulic Experiments...................4to,   15 00
Franzen, H.   Exercises in Gas Analysis......................12mo,   *1 00
Fraser, E. S., and Jones, R. B.   Motor Vehicles and Their Motors,
8vo, fabrikoid,   2 00
Frederick, R. C., and Forster, A.   Public Health Chemical Analysis..8vo,   4 50
Freudemacher, P. W.   Electric Mining Installations...........12mo,   1 00
Friend, J. N.   The Chemistry of Linseed Oil.................12mo,   1 00
Fritsch, J.   Manufacture of Chemical Manures 8vo,   6 00
Frye, A. I.   Civil Engineers' Pocket-book.............. 12mo, leather,   *5 00
Fuller, G. W.   Investigations into the Purification of the Ohio River.
4to,   *10 00
Furnell, J.   Paints, Colors, Oils, and Varnishes.................8vo.

Ganswindt, A.   Dyeing Silk, Mixed Silk Fabrics and Artificial Silks,
8vo,   5 00
Gant, L. W.   Elements of Electric Traction....................8vo,   *2 50
Garcia, A. J. R. V.   Spanish-English Railway Terms...........8vo,   3 00
Gardner, H. A.   Paint Researches, and Their Practical Applications,
8vo,   *5 00
Garforth, W. E.   Rules for Recovering Coal Mines after Explosions and
Fires.......................................12mo, leather,   1 50
Garrard, C. C.   Electric Switch and Controlling Gear...........8vo,   10 00
Gaudard, J.   Foundations...................................16mo,   0 75
Gear, H. B., and Williams, P. F.   Electric Central Station Distribution
Systems 8vo,   *3 50
Geerligs, H. C. P.   Cane Sugar and Its Manufacture. 8vo. (Reprinting.)
—— Chemical Control in Cane Sugar Factories.................4to,   5 00
Geikie, J.   Structural and Field Geology.....................8vo,   7 50
Georgi, F., and Schubert, A.   Sheet Metal Working...........8vo,   3 50
Gerhard, W. P.   Sanitation, Watersupply and Sewage Disposal of Country
Houses 12mo,   2 50

—— Gas Lighting ....16mo,   o 75
—— Household Wastes ....16mo,   o 75
—— House Drainage ....16mo,   o 75
—— Sanitary Drainage of Buildings...........................16mo,   o 75
Gerhardi, C. W. H.   Electricity Meters......................8vo,   *7 20
Gibbings, A. H.   Oil Fuel Equipment for Locomotives. 8vo.
                                                    (*Reprinting.*)
Gibbs, W. E.   Lighting by Acetylene...........................12mo,   *1 50
Gibson, A. H.   Hydraulics and Its Application..................8vo,   6 oo
—— Water Hammer in Hydraulic Pipe Lines......12mo. (*Reprinting.*)
Gibson, A. H., and Ritchie, E. G.   Circular Arc Bow Girder........4to,   *3 50
Gilbreth, F. B.   Motion Study................................12mo,   *2 oo
——- Primer of Scientific Management..........................12mo,   1 25
Gill, A. H.   Gas Analysis for Chemists........................8vo,   1 25
Gillmore, Gen. Q. A.   Roads, Streets, and Pavements...........12mo,   1 25
Godfrey, E.   Tables for Structural Engineers..........16mo, leather,   *2 50
Golding, H. A.   The Theta-Phi Diagram......................12mo,   *2 oo
Goodchild, W.   Precious Stones...............................8vo,   2 50
Goodell, J. M.   The Location, Construction and Maintenance of
        Roads ....8vo,   2 oo
Goodeve, T. M.   Textbook on the Steam-engine...............12mo,   2 50
Gore, G.   Electrolytic Separation of Metals.....................8vo,   4 50
Gornston, M. H.   The Operating Engineers' Catechism...(*In Press.*)
Gould, E. S.   Arithmetic of the Steam-engine..................12mo,   1 oo
—— Calculus ....16mo,   o 75
—— High Masonry Dams.....................................16mo,   o 75
Gould, E. S.   Practical Hydrostatics and Hydrostatic Formulas..16mo,   o 75
Goulding, E.   Cotton and Other Vegetable Fibres...............8vo,   3 oo
Gratacap, L. P.   A Popular Guide to Minerals..................8vo,   3 oo
Gray, H. H.   Gas-Works Products....................8vo (*In Press.*)
Gray, J.   Electrical Influence Machines.......................12mo,   2 oo
—— Marine Boiler Design.......................................8vo,   3 oo
Greenhill, G.   Dynamics of Mechanical Flight..................8vo,   *2 50
Greenwood, H. C.   The Industrial Gases......................8vo,   5 oo
Gregorius, R.   Mineral Waxes...............................12mo,   3 oo
Grierson, R.   Some Modern Methods of Ventilation..............8vo,   *3 oo
Griffith, E. A.   Engineering Instruments and Meters............8vo,   6 50
Griffiths, A. B.   A Treatise on Manures..........12mo (*Reprinting.*)
Gross, E.   Hops..8vo,   *5 oo
Grossman, J.   Ammonia and Its Compounds..................12mo,   1 50
Groth, L. A.   Welding and Cutting Metals by Gases or Electricity.
                                                             8vo,   3 oo
Gruner, A.   Power-loom Weaving..............................8vo,   *3 50
Grunsky, C. E.   Topographic Stadia Surveying................16mo,   2 oo
Gunther, C. O.   Integration...................................8vo,   1 50
Gurden, R. L.   Traverse Tables................................folio,   7 50
Guy, A. E.   Experiments on the Flexure of Beams...............8vo,   *1 25

Haenig, A.   Emery and Emery Industry......................8vo,   *2 50
Hainbach, R.   Pottery Decoration............................12mo,   3 50
Hale, A. J.   The Manufacture of Chemicals by Electrolysis......8vo,   2 oo

Hale, Harrison. American Chemistry...........................12mo,   2 00
Hale, W. J. Calculations of General Chemistry...............12mo,   1 50
Hall, C. H. Chemistry of Paints and Paint Vehicles..............12mo,   *2 00
Hall, R. H. Governors and Governing Mechanism..............12mo,   *2 50
Hall, W. S. Elements of the Differential and Integral Calculus....8vo,   2 75
——Descriptive Geometry..............8vo volume and a 4to atlas,   4 00
Haller, G. F., and Cunningham, E. T. The Tesla Coil............12mo,   *1 25
Halsey, F. A. Slide Valve Gears.................................12mo,   1 50
——The Use of the Slide Rules............................16mo,   0 75
—— Worm and Spiral Gearing................................16mo,   0 75
Hamlin, M. L. Action of Chemicals on Industrial Materials..8vo,
(*In Press.*)
Hancock, H. Textbook of Mechanics and Hydrostatics...........8vo,   1 50
Hardy, E. Elementary Principles of Graphic Statics.............12mo,   *1 50
Haring, H. Engineering Law.
Vol. I. Law of Contract....................................8vo,   *4 00
Harper, J. H. Hydraulic Tables on the Flow of Water........16mo,   *2 00
Harris, S. M. Practical Topographical Surveying.........(*In Press.*)
Harrow, B. Eminent Chemists of Our Times.................. 12mo,   2 50
——From Newton to Einstein...............................12mo,   1 00
Harvey, A. Practical Leather Chemistry.......................8vo,   3 75
Haskins, C. H. The Galvanometer and Its Uses.................16mo,   1 50
Hatt, J. A. H. The Colorist...........................square 12mo,   *1 50
Hausbrand, E. Drying by Means of Air and Steam.............12mo,   2 50
—— Evaporating, Condensing and Cooling Apparatus.............8vo,   6 00
Hausmann, E. Telegraph Engineering..........................8vo,   *3 00
Hausner, A. Manufacture of Preserved Foods and Sweetmeats....8vo,   3 50
Hawkesworth, J. Graphical Handbook for Reinforced Concrete Design.
4to,   2 00
Hay, A. Continuous Current Engineering......................8vo,   3 75
Hayes, H. V. Public Utilities, Their Cost New and Depreciation...8vo,   *2 00
—— Public Utilities, Their Fair Present Value and Return......8vo,   *2 00
Heath, F. H. Chemistry of Photography..............8vo. (*In Press.*)
Heather, H. J. S. Electrical Engineering......................8vo,   4 50
Heaviside, O. Electromagnetic Theory. Vols. I and II....8vo, each,
(*Reprinting.*)
Vol. III......................................8vo (*Reprinting.*)
Heck, R. C. H. The Steam Engine and the Turbine............8vo,   4 50
—— Steam-Engine and Other Steam Motors. Two Volumes.
Vol. I. Thermodynamics and the Mechanics................8vo,   4 50
Vol. II. Form, Construction, and Working................8vo,   5 50
—— Notes on Elementary Kinematics...................8vo, boards,   *1 00
—— Graphics of Machine Forces...........................8vo, boards,   *1 00
Heermann, P. Dyers' Materials...............................12mo,   3 00
Henderson, I. F. A Dictionary of Scientific Terms..............8vo,   4 50
Hering, C., and Getman, F. H. Standard Tables of Electro-Chemical
Equivalents 12mo,   *2 00
Hering, D. W. Essentials of Physics for College Students.......8vo,   2 25
Herington, C. F. Powdered Coal as Fuel.....................8vo,   4 50
Herrmann, G. The Graphical Statics of Mechanism............12mo,   2 00
Herzfeld, J. Testing of Yarns and Textile Fabrics...........8vo.
(*New Edition in Preparation.*)
Hildenbrand, B. W. Cable-Making.............................16mo,   0 75

Hilditch, T. P.   A Concise History of Chemistry..............12mo,   *1 50
Hill, M. J. M.   The Theory of Proportion......................8vo,   *2 50
Hillhouse, P. A.   Ship Stability and Trim....................8vo,   5 00
Hiroi, I.   Plate Girder Construction...........................16mo,   0 75
—— Statically-Indeterminate Stresses.........................12mo,   2 50
Hirshfeld, C. F.   Engineering Thermodynamics.................16mo,   0 75
Hoar, A.   The Submarine Torpedo Boat.......................12mo,   *2 00
Hobart, H. M.   Heavy Electrical Engineering..................8vo,   *4 50
—— Design of Static Transformers............................12mo,   2 50
—— Electricity.......   ....8vo,   *2 00
—— Electric Trains.............................8vo (*Reprinting.*)
—— Electric Propulsion of Ships...............................8vo,   *2 50
Hobart, J. F.   Hard Soldering, Soft Soldering and Brazing.....12mo,   1 25
Hobbs, W. R. P.   The Arithmetic of Electrical Measurements....12mo,   0 75
Hoff, J. N.   Paint and Varnish Facts and Formulas............12mo,   2 00
Hole, W.   The Distribution of Gas............................8vo,   7 50
Holmes, A.   Nomenclature of Petrology........................8vo,   3 50
Hopkins, N. M.   Model Engines and Small Boats..............12mo,   1 25
—— The Outlook for Research and Invention...............12mo,   2 00
Hopkinson, J., Shoolbred, J. N., and Day, R. E.   Dynamic Electricity.
                                                                16mo.   0 75
Horner, J.   Practical Ironfounding.............................8vo,   *2 00
—— Gear Cutting, in Theory and Practice........8vo (*Reprinting.*)
Houghton, C. E.   The Elements of Mechanics of Materials.....12mo,   2 50
Houstoun, R. A.   Studies in Light Production..................12mo,   2 00
Hovenden, F.   Practical Mathematics for Young Engineers......12mo,   *1 50
Howe, G.   Mathematics for the Practical Man.................12mo,   1 50
Howorth, J.   Repairing and Riveting Glass, China and Earthenware.
                                                          8vo, paper,   *0 50
Hoyt, W. E.   Chemistry by Experimentation...................8vo,   *0 70
Hubbard, E.   The Utilization of Wood-waste....................8vo,   4 50
Hübner, J.   Bleaching and Dyeing of Vegetable and Fibrous Materials.
                                                                8vo,   7 50
Hudson, O. F.   Iron and Steel..................................8vo,   3 00
Humphreys, A. C.   The Business Features of Engineering Practice.8vo,   2 50
Hunter, A.   Bridge Work.........................8vo. (*In Press.*)
Hurst, G. H.   Handbook of the Theory of Color................8vo,   *3 50
—— Dictionary of Chemicals and Raw Products................8vo,   *5 00
—— Lubricating Oils, Fats and Greases.........................8vo,   *5 00
—— Soaps 8vo,   *6 00
Hurst G. H., and Simmons, W. H.   Textile Soaps and Oils......8vo,   4 00
Hurst, H. E., and Lattey, R. T.   Text-book of Physics..........8vo,   *3 00
—— Also published in three parts.
    Part I.   Dynamics and Heat.....................................   1 50
    Part II.   Sound and Light......................................   1 50
    Part III.   Magnetism and Electricity............................   2 00
Hutchinson, R. W., Jr.   Long Distance Electric Power Transmission.
                                                                12mo,   3 00
Hutchinson, R. W., Jr., and Thomas, W. A.   Electricity in Mining.12mo,
                                                          (*In Press.*)
Hyde, E. W.   Skew Arches.....................................16mo.   0 75

Luckiesh, M. Color and Its Application........................8vo,   4 50
—— Light and Shade and Their Applications..................8vo,   3 00
—— Visual Illusions...............................(*In Preparation.*)
Lunge, G. Coal-tar and Ammonia. Three Volumes.............8vo, *25 00
—— Technical Gas Analysis.....................................8vo,   *4 50
—— Manufacture of Sulphuric Acid and Alkali. Four Volumes....8vo,
   Vol. I. Sulphuric Acid. In three parts...........(*Reprinting.*)
   Vol. I. Supplement ....8vo (*Reprinting.*)
   Vol. II. Salt Cake, Hydrochloric Acid and Leblanc Soda. In two
     parts ....(*In Press.*)
   Vol. III. Ammonia Soda.............................(*In Press.*)
   Vol. IV. Electrolytic Methods......................(*In Press.*)
—— Technical Chemists' Handbook...................12mo, leather,   *4 00
—— Technical Methods of Chemical Analysis.
   Vol. I. In two parts.............8vo (*New Edition in Press.*)
   Vol. II. In two parts.............8vo (*New Edition in Press.*)
   Vol. III. In two parts............8vo (*New Edition in Press.*)
   The set (3 vols.) complete........
Luquer, L. M. Minerals in Rock Sections......................8vo,   1 75
MacBride, J. D. A Handbook of Practical Shipbuilding,
                   12mo, fabrikoid,   3 00
Mackenzie, N. F. Notes on Irrigation Works...................8vo,   *2 50
Mackie, J. How to Make a Woolen Mill Pay..................8vo,   *2 00
Maguire, Wm. R. Domestic Sanitary Drainage and Plumbing 8vo,   4 00
Malcolm, H. W. Submarine Telegraph Cable......................   9 00
Malinovzsky, A. Ceramics.....................................12mo,   3 00
Mallet, A. Compound Engines..................................16mo,
Mansfield, A. N. Electro-magnets.............................16mo,   0 75
Marks, E. C. R. Construction of Cranes and Lifting Machinery.12mo,   *2 75
—— Manufacture of Iron and Steel Tubes.......................12mo,   2 50
—— Mechanical Engineering Materials..........................12mo,   *1 50
Marks, G. C. Hydraulic Power Engineering.....................8vo,   4 50
Marsh, C. F. Concise Treatise on Reinforced Concrete 8vo,   *2 50
—— Reinforced Concrete Compression Member Diagram. Mounted on
   Cloth Boards..   *1.50
Marsh, C. F., and Dunn, W. Manual of Reinforced Concrete and Con-
   crete Block Construction.............................16mo,   2 00
Marshall, W. J., and Sankey, H. R. Gas Engines..............8vo,   2 00
Martin, G. Triumphs and Wonders of Modern Chemistry......8vo,   *3 00
—— Modern Chemistry and Its Wonders....................8vo,   *3 00
Martin, N. Properties and Design of Reinforced Concrete........8vo,   1 50
Martin, W. D. Hints to Engineers...........................12mo,   2 00
Massie, W. W., and Underhill, C. R. Wireless Telegraphy and Telephony.
                   12mo,   *1 00
Mathot, R. E. Internal Combustion Engines...................8vo,   5 00
Maurice, W. Electric Blasting Apparatus and Explosives... ....8vo,   *3 50
—— Shot Firer's Guide.......... .... 8vo,   *1 50
Maxwell, F. Sulphitation in White Sugar Manufacture.......12mo,   4 00
Maxwell, J. C. Matter and Motion............................16mo,   0 75

Maxwell, W. H., and Brown, J. T. Encyclopedia of Municipal and Sanitary Engineering..4to, *10 00
Mayer, A. M. Lecture Notes on Physics.......................8vo, 2 00
McCracken, E. M., and Sampson, C. H. Course in Pattern Making.
　　　　　　　　　　　　　　　　　　　　　　　　　　　4to, 2 00
McCullough, E. Practical Surveying...........................12mo, 3 00
McCullough, R. S. Mechanical Theory of Heat................8vo, 3 50
McGibbon, W. C. Indicator Diagrams for Marine Engineers......8vo, 5 00
—— Marine Engineers' Drawing Book....................oblong 4to, *2 50
McGibbon, W. C. Marine Engineers Pocketbook...............12mo, * 4 50
McIntosh, J. G. Technology of Sugar.........................8vo, *6 00
—— Industrial Alcohol 8vo, *3 50
—— Manufacture of Varnishes and Kindred Industries. Three Volumes.
　　　8vo.
　　　Vol. I. Oil Crushing, Refining and Boiling.................... 7 00
　　　Vol. II. Varnish Materials and Oil Varnish Making............ 5 00
　　　Vol. III. Spirit Varnishes and Materials..................... 6 00
McKillop, M., and McKillop, A. D. Efficiency Methods.........12mo, 1 50
McKnight, J. D., and Brown, A. W. Marine Multitubular Boilers.... *2 50
McMaster, J. B. Bridge and Tunnel Centres.................16mo, 0 75
McMechen, F. L. Tests for Ores, Minerals and Metals........12mo, 1 50
McNair, F. V. Handbook for Naval Officers...................12mo, 4 00
Meade, A. Modern Gas Works Practice........................8vo, *8 50
Melick, C. W. Dairy Laboratory Guide......................12mo, *1 25
"Mentor." Self-Instruction for Students in Gas Supply. 12mo.
　　　Elementary ....
　　　Advanced 2 50
—— Self-Instruction for Students in Gas Engineering. 12mo. 2 50
　　　Elementary ....
　　　Advanced 2 00
Merivale, J. H. Notes and Formulae for Mining Students......12mo, 2 00
Merritt, Wm. H. Field Testing for Gold and Silver....16mo, leather, 1 00
Mertens. Tactics and Technique of River Crossings............8vo, 2 00
Mierzinski, S. Waterproofing of Fabrics.....................8vo, 3 00
Miessner, B. F. Radio Dynamics.............................8vo, 2 50
Miller, G. A. Determinants.................................12mo, *2 00
Miller, W. J. Introduction to Historical Geology............12mo,
Mills, C. N. Elementary Mechanics for Engineers.............8vo, 2 50
Mills, John. Within the Atom....................12mo (In Press.) 1 25
Milroy, M. E. W. Home Lace-making.........................12mo, *1 00
—— Church Lace 12mo, 2 50
Mitchell, C. A. Mineral and Aerated Waters..................8vo, *3 00
Mitchell, C. A., and Prideaux, R. M. Fibres Used in Textile and Allied
　　　Industries 8vo, 3 50
Mitchell, C. F., and G. A. Building Construction and Drawing. 12mo.
　　　Elementary Course 2 50
　　　Advanced Course 4 50
Monckton, C. C. F. Radiotelegraphy...........................8vo, 2 00
Monteverde. R. D. Vest Pocket Glossary of English-Spanish, Spanish-
　　　English Technical Terms.....................64mo, leather, 1 50
Montgomery, J. H. Electric Wiring Specifications............16mo, 1 00
Moore, E. C. S. New Tables for the Complete Solution of Ganguillet and
　　　Kutter's Formula 8vo, *6 00
Moore, Harold. Liquid Fuel for Internal Combustion Engines...8vo, 5 00

Morecroft, J. H., and Hehre, F. W.   Short Course in Electrical Testing.
8vo, 2 00

Morgan, A. P. Wireless Telegraph Construction for Amateurs..12mo, 1 50
Morrell, R. S., and Waele, A. E. Rubber, Resins, Paints and Varnishes 8vo, 4 00
Moses, A. J. The Characters of Crystals.......................8vo, *2 00
——and Parsons, C. L. Elements of Mineralogy.................8vo, 4 50
Moss, S. A. Elements of Gas Engine Design.................16mo, 0 75
—— The Lay-out of Corliss Valve Gears.....................16mo, 0 75
Mulford, A. C. Boundaries and Landmarks...................12mo, 1 00
Munby, A. E. Chemistry and Physics of Building Materials....8vo, 2 50
Murphy, J. G. Practical Mining............................16mo, 1 00
Murray, B. M. Chemical Reagents...........................8vo, 3 00
Murray, J. A. Soils and Manures...........................8vo, 2 00

Nasmith, J. The Student's Cotton Spinning...................8vo, 5 00
—— Recent Cotton Mill Construction.........................12mo, 3 00
Neave, G. B., and Heilbron, I. M. Identification of Organic Compounds.
12mo, 1 50
Neilson, R. M. Aeroplane Patents...........................8vo, *2 00
Nerz, F. Searchlights...........................8vo *(Reprinting.)*
Newbigin, M. I., and Flett, J. S. James Geikie, the Man and the Geologist.............................. ....8vo, 3 50
Newbiging, T. Handbook for Gas Engineers and Managers......8vo, 7 50
Newell, F. H., and Drayer, C. E. Engineering as a Career..12mo, cloth, *1 00
Nicol, G. Ship Construction and Calculations...................8vo, 7 50
Nipher, F. E. Theory of Magnetic Measurements.............12mo, 1 00
Nisbet, H. Grammar of Textile Design.......................8vo, 7 50
Nolan, H. The Telescope.....................................16mo, 0 75
Norie, J. W. Epitome of Navigation (2 Vols.)................octavo, 15 00
—— A Complete Set of Nautical Tables with Explanations of Their Use ....octavo, 6 50
North, H. B. Laboratory Experiments in General Chemistry.....12mo, *1 00

O'Connor, H. The Gas Engineer's Pocketbook..........12mo, leather, 5 00
Ohm, G. S., and Lockwood, T. D. Galvanic Circuit............16mo, 0 75
Olsen, J. C. Text-book of Quantitative Chemical Analysis.....8vo, 4 00
Ormsby, M. T. M. Surveying.................................12mo, 2 00
Oudin, M. A. Standard Polyphase Apparatus and Systems........8vo, *3 00

Pakes, W. C. C., and Nankivell, A. T. The Science of Hygiene ..8vo, *1 75
Palaz, A. Industrial Photometry...............................8vo, 5 00
Palmer, A. R. Electrical Experiments........................12mo, 0 75
—— Magnetic Measurements and Experiments.................12mo, 0 75
Pamely, C. Colliery Manager's Handbook.....................8vo, *10 00
Parker, P. A. M. The Control of Water.......................8vo, 6 00
Parr, G. D. A. Electrical Engineering Measuring Instruments....8vo, *3 50
Parry, E. J. Chemistry of Essential Oils and Artificial Perfumes.
   Vol. I.   Monographs on Essential Oils......................... 9 00
   Vol. II. Constituents of Essential Oils, Analysis.............. 7 00
—— Foods and Drugs. Two Volumes.
   Vol. I.   The Analysis of Food and Drugs.................8vo, 9 50
   Vol. II. The Sale of Food and Drugs Acts...............8vo, 3 50
—— and Coste, J. H. Chemistry of Pigments....................8vo, *5 00

Prelini, C.   Earth and Rock Excavation..........................8vo,   *3 00
—— Graphical Determination of Earth Slopes....................8vo,   *2 00
—— Tunneling.   New Edition.............................8vo,   *3 00
—— Dredging.   A Practical Treatise........................8vo,   *3 00
Prescott, A. B., and Johnson, O. C.   Qualitative Chemical Analysis..8vo,   4 00
Prescott, A. B., and Sullivan, E. C.   First Book in Qualitative Chemistry.   1 50
Prideaux, E. B. R.   Problems in Physical Chemistry...........8vo,   4 50
—— The Theory and Use of Indicators.........................8vo,   5 00
Prince, G. T.   Flow of Water...............................12mo,   *2 00
Pull, E.   Modern Steam Boilers..............................8vo,   5 00
Pullen, W. W. F.   Application of Graphic Methods to the Design of
      Structures 12mo,   3 00
—— Injectors: Theory, Construction and Working.............12mo,   *2 00
—— Indicator Diagrams 8vo,   3 00
—— Engine Testing 8vo,   *5 50
Purday, H. F. P.   The Diesel Engine Design....................8vo,   7 50

Rafter, G. W.   Mechanics of Ventilation.......................16mo,   0 75
—— Potable Water 16mo,   0 75
—— Treatment of Septic Sewage..............................16mo,   0 75
—— and Baker, M. N.   Sewage Disposal in the United States....4to,   6 00
Raikes, H. P.   Sewage Disposal Works 8vo,   *4 00
Randau, P.   Enamels and Enamelling.........................8vo,   *5 00
Rankine, W. J. M.   A Manual of Applied Mechanics............8vo,   6 00
—— Civil Engineering 8vo.   7 50
—— Machinery and Millwork....................................8vo,   6 00
—— The Steam-engine and Other Prime Movers.................8vo,   6 00
Raphael, F. C.   Localization of Faults in Electric Light and Power Mains.
                                                          8vo,   5 00
Rasch, E.   Electric Arc Phenomena..........................8vo,   2 00
Rathbone, R. L. B.   Simple Jewellery.........................8vo,   2 50
Rausenberger, F.   The Theory of the Recoil Guns..............8vo,   *5 00
Rautenstrauch, W.   Notes on the Elements of Machine Design.8vo, boards,   *1 50
Rautenstrauch, W., and Williams, J. T.   Machine Drafting and Empirical
      Design.
      Part I. Machine Drafting...............................8vo,   1 50
      Part II. Empirical Design.....................(In Preparation.)
Raymond, E. B.   Alternating Current Engineering..............12mo,   *2 50
Rayner, H.   Silk Throwing and Waste Silk Spinning............8vo,   5 00
Recipes for the Color, Paint, Varnish, Oil, Soap and Drysaltery Trades,
                                                          8vo,   *5 00
Recipes for Flint Glass Making..............................12mo,   *5 00
Redfern, J. B., and Savin, J.   Bells, Telephones................16mo,   0 75
Redgrove, H. S.   Experimental Mensuration..................12mo,   1 50
Reed, E. G.   The Transformers........................(In Press.)
Reed, S.   Turbines Applied to Marine Propulsion....................   *5 00
Reed's Engineers' Handbook....................................8vo,   9 00
—— Key to the Nineteenth Edition of Reed's Engineers' Handbook.8vo,   3 50
—— Useful Hints to Sea-going Engineers......................12mo,   2 50
Reeve, F. C.   Elementary Qualitative Analysis of the Metals and Acid
      Radicals 12mo,   1 50
Reid, E. E.   Introduction to Research in Organic Chemistry. (In Press.)

Reinhardt, C. W.   Lettering for Draftsmen, Engineers, and Students.
oblong 4to, boards,   1 25
Reinhardt, C. W.   The Technic of Mechanical Drafting,
oblong, 4to, boards,   *1 00
Reiser, F.   Hardening and Tempering of Steel..................12mo,   2 50
Reiser, N.   Faults in the Manufacture of Woolen Goods........8vo,   2 50
—— Spinning and Weaving Calculations......................8vo,   *5 00
Renwick, W. G.   Marble and Marble Working.................8vo,   6 50
Reuleaux, F.   The Constructor...................................4to,   4 00
Rey, Jean.   The Range of Electric Searchlight Projectors.......:.8vo,   4 50
Reynolds, O., and Idell, F. E.   Triple Expansion Engines........16mo,   0 75
Rhead, G. F.   Simple Structural Woodwork..................12mo,   *1 25
Rhead, G. W.   British Pottery Marks..........................8vo,   3 50
Rhodes, H. J.   Art of Lithography...............................8vo,   5 00
Rice, J. M and Johnson, W. W.   A New Method of Obtaining the Differ-
ential of Functions...................................12mo,   0 50
Richards, E. G.   Experience Grading and Rating Schedule........8vo   4 00
Richards, W. A.   Forging of Iron and Steel...................12mo   2 25
Richards, W. A., and North, H. B.   Manual of Cement Testing....12mo,   *1 50
Richardson, J.   The Modern Steam Engine......................8vo,   *3 50
Richardson, S. S.   Magnetism and Electricity....................12mo,   *2 00
Rideal, E. K.   Industrial Electrometallurgy....................8vo,   3 00
—— The Rare Earths and Metals...................8vo (In Press.)
—— Ozone 8vo,   4 00
Rideal, S.   Glue and Glue Testing.............................8vo,   *5 00
—— The Carbohydrates 8vo,   4 00
Riesenberg, F.   The Men on Deck..............................12mo,   3 00
—— Standard Seamanship for the Merchant Marine. 12mo (In Press.)
Rimmer, E. J.   Boiler Explosions, Collapses and Mishaps......8vo,   2 25
Rings, F.   Reinforced Concrete in Theory and Practice.........12mo,   *4 50
Ripper, W.   Course of Instruction in Machine Drawing...........folio,   *6 00
Roberts, F. C.   Figure of the Earth.............................16mo,   0 75
Roberts, J., Jr.   Laboratory Work in Electrical Engineering.......8vo,   *2 00
Robertson, J. B.   The Chemistry of Coal....................12mo,   1 25
Robertson, L. S.   Water-tube Boilers..........................8vo,   2 00
Robinson, J. B.   Architectural Composition....................8vo,   3 50
Robinson, S. W.   Practical Treatise on the Teeth of Wheels..16mo,   0 75
—— Railroad Economics 16mo,   0 75
—— Wrought Iron Bridge Members............................16mo,   0 75
Robson, J. H.   Machine Drawing and Sketching.................8vo,   *2 00
Roebling, J. A.   Long and Short Span Railway Bridges.........folio.   25 00
Rogers, A.   A Laboratory Guide of Industrial Chemistry........8vo,   2 00
—— Elements of Industrial Chemistry........................12mo,   *3 00
—— Manual of Industrial Chemistry..........................8vo,   7 50
Rogers, F.   Magnetism of Iron Vessels........................16mo,   0 75
Rohland, P.   Colloidal and Crystalloidal State of Matter......12mo,
(Reprinting.)
Rollinson, C.   Alphabets ....Oblong, 12mo,   1 25
Rose, J.   The Pattern-makers' Assistant.......................8vo,   2 50
—— Key to Engines and Engine-running.....................12mo,   2 50
Rose, T. K.   The Precious Metals...............................8vo,   2 50

Rosenhain, W. Glass Manufacture............................8vo,   4 00
—— Physical Metallurgy, An Introduction to...................8vo,   4 00
Roth, W. A. Physical Chemistry............................8vo,   *2 00
Rowan, F. J., and Idell, F. E. Boiler Incrustation and Corrosion.16mo,   0 75
Roxburgh, W. General Foundry Practice.....................8vo,   2 50
Ruhmer, E. Wireless Telephony..............................8vo,   4 50
Russell, A. Theory of Electric Cables and Network.............8vo,   5 00
Rust, A. Practical Tables for Navigators and Aviators.........8vo,   3 50
Rutley, F. Elements of Mineralogy...........................12mo,   2 50

Sandeman, E. A. Notes on the Manufacture of Earthenware...12mo,   3 50
Sanford, P. G. Nitro-explosives................................8vo,   *4 00
Saunders, C. H. Handbook of Practical Mechanics...........16mo,   1 50
                                                        leather,   2 00
Sayers, H. M. Brakes for Tram Cars.........................8vo,   *1 25
Schaefer, C. T. Motor Truck Design.........................8vo,   2 50
Scheithauer, W. Shale Oils and Tars.........................8vo,   *4 00
Scherer, R. Casein..8vo,   3 50
Schidrowitz, P. Rubber, Its Production and Industrial Uses......8vo,   *6 00
Schindler, K. Iron and Steel Construction Works............12mo,   *2 00
Schmall, C. N. First Course in Analytic Geometry, Plane and Solid.
                                                        12mo,   2 00
—— and Shack, S. M. Elements of Plane Geometry..........12mo,   1 25
Schmeer, L. Flow of Water...................................8vo,   1 50
Schwarz, E. H. L. Causal Geology............................8vo,   *3 00
Schweizer, V. Distillations of Resins...........................8vo,   5 00
Scott, A. H. Reinforced Concrete in Practice.................12mo,   2 00
Scott, W. W. Qualitative Analysis. A Laboratory Manual. New
        Edition 3 00
—— Standard Methods of Chemical Analysis...................8vo,   7 50
Scribner, J. M. Engineers' and Mechanics' Companion..16mo, leather,   1 50
Scudder, H. Electrical Conductivity and Ionization Constants of
        Organic Compounds.......... ....8vo,   *3 00
Seamanship, Lectures on..12mo,   2 00
Searle, A. B. Modern Brickmaking.............................8vo,   7 00
—— Cement, Concrete and Bricks...............................8vo,   3 00
Searle, G. M. "Sumners' Method." Condensed and Improved.
                                                        16mo,   0 75
Seaton, A. E. Manual of Marine Engineering..................8vo,   10 00
Seaton, A. E., and Rounthwaite, H. M. Pocket-book of Marine Engi-
        neering ....16mo, leather,   6 00
Seeligmann, T., Torrilhon, G. L., and Falconnet, H. India Rubber and
        Gutta Percha 8vo,   6 00
Seidell, A. Solubilities of Inorganic and Organic Substances....8vo,   7 50
Sellew, W. H. Steel Rails......................................4to, *10 00
—— Railway Maintenance Engineering.........................12mo,   3 00
Senter, G. Outlines of Physical Chemistry....................12mo,   3 00
—— Text-book of Inorganic Chemistry.........................12mo,   *3 00
Sever, G. F. Electric Engineering Experiments...........8vo, boards,   *1 00
Sever, G. F., and Townsend, F. Laboratory and Factory Tests in Elec-
        trical Engineering...... ....8vo,   *2 50
Sewall, C. H. Wireless Telegraphy.............................8vo,   *2 00
—— Lessons in Telegraphy......................................12mo,   *1 00
Sexton, A. H. Chemistry of the Materials of Engineering........12mo,   3 00
—— Alloys (Non-Ferrous) 8vo,   3 50

Sexton, A. H., and Primrose, J. S. G. The Metallurgy of Iron and Steel.
8vo,   6 50
—— The Common Metals (Non-Ferrous)......................8vo,   4 00
Seymour, A. Modern Printing Inks...........................8vo,   3 00
Shaw, Henry S. H. Mechanical Integrators..................16mo,   0 75
Shaw, J. B. Vector Calculus...........................(*In Press.*)
Shaw, T. R. Driving of Machine Tools....................12mo,   *2 00
—— Precision Grinding Machines............................12mo,   5 00
Shaw, W. N. Forecasting Weather............—..8vo (*Reprinting.*)
Sheldon, S., and Hausmann, E. Dynamo Electric Machinery, A.C.
and D.C...................................8vo (*In Press.*)
—— Electric Traction and Transmission Engineering.........12mo,   3 00
—— Physical Laboratory Experiments, for Engineering Students..8vo,   1 50
Sherriff, F. F. Oil Merchants' Manual and Oil Trade Ready Reckoner,
8vo,   3 50
Shields, J. E. Notes on Engineering Construction..............12mo,   1 50
Shreve, S. H. Strength of Bridges and Roofs..................8vo,   3 50
Shunk, W. F. The Field Engineer ....12mo, fabrikoid,   3 00
Silverman, A., and Harvey, A. W. Laboratory Directions and Study
Questions in Inorganic Chemistry:...........4to, loose leaf,   2 00
Simmons, H. E. Rubber Manufacture...........................4to,   4 50
Simmons, W. H. Fats, Waxes and Essential Oils..8vo (*In Press.*)
Simmons, W. H., and Appleton, H. A. Handbook of Soap Manufacture,
8vo,   *4 00
Simmons, W. H., and Mitchell, C. A. Edible Fats and Oils......8vo,   *3 50
Simpson, G. The Naval Constructor.................12mo, fabrikoid,   *5 00
Simpson, W. Foundations........................8vo. (*In Press.*)
Sinclair, A. Development of the Locomotive Engine...8vo, half leather,   5 00
Sindall, R. W. Manufacture of Paper........................8vo,   3 00
Sindall, R. W., and Bacon, W. N. The Testing of Wood Pulp....8vo,   2 50
—— Wood and Cellulose............................8vo (*In Press.*)
Sloane, T. O'C. Elementary Electrical Calculations...........12mo,   2 50
—— Short-Cuts in Arithmetic...........................(*In Press.*)
Smallwood, J. C. Mechanical Laboratory Methods....12mo, fabrikoid,   3 00
Smith, C. A. M. Handbook of Testing, MATERIALS............8vo,   5 00
Smith, C. A. M., and Warren, A. G. New Steam Tables........8vo,   1 00
Smith, C. F. Practical Alternating Currents and Testing........8vo,   *3 50
—— Practical Testing of Dynamos and Motors............... 8vo,   *3 00
Smith, F. E. Handbook of General Instruction for Mechanics...12mo,   1 50
Smith, G. C. Trinitrotoluenes and Mono- and Dinitrotoluenes, Their
Manufacture and Properties...........................12mo,   2 00
Smith, H. G. Minerals and the Microscope....................12mo,   2 00
Smith, J. C. Manufacture of Paint...........................8vo,   *5 00
Smith, R. H. Principles of Machine Work..................12mo,
—— Advanced Machine Work..............................12mo,   3 00
Smith, W. Chemistry of Hat Manufacturing................12mo,   *3 50
Snell, F. D. Colorimetric Analysis ....12mo (*In Press.*)
Snow, W. G., and Nolan, T. Ventilation of Buildings........16mo,   0 75
Soddy, F. Radioactivity.........................8vo (*Reprinting.*)
Solomon, M. Electric Lamps...................................8vo,   2 00
Somerscales, A. N. Mechanics for Marine Engineers..........12mo.   2 50
—— Mechanical and Marine Engineering Science.................8vo,   *5 00

Sothern, J. W. The Marine Steam Turbine....................8vo,   15 00
—— Verbal Notes and Sketches for Marine Engineers..........8vo,   15 00
—— Marine Engine Indicator Cards....................8vo,   4 50
—— Oil Fuel Burning in Marine Practice......................8vo,   7 50
Sothern, J. W., and Sothern, R. M. Simple Problems in Marine
    Engineering Design 12mo,   3 00
Souster, E. G. W. Design of Factory and Industrial Buildings...8vo,   4 00
Southcombe, J. E. Chemistry of the Oil Industries............8vo,   3 50
Soxhlet, D. H. Dyeing and Staining Marble...................8vo,   2 50
Spangenburg, L. Fatigue of Metals..........................16mo,   0 75
Specht, G. J., Hardy, A. S., McMaster, J. B., and Walling. Topographical
    Surveying 16mo,   0 75
Spencer, A. S. Design of Steel-Framed Sheds.................8vo,   *3 50
Spiegel, L. Chemical Constitution and Physiological Action....12mo,   1 25
Sprague, E. H. Hydraulics..................................12mo,   2 00
—— Elements of Graphic Statics.............................8vo,   2 00
—— Stability of Masonry....................................12mo,   2 00
—— Elementary Mathematics for Engineers...................12mo,   2 00
—— Stability of Arches.....................................12mo,   2 00
—— Strength of Structural Elements........................12mo,   2 00
—— Moving Loads by Influence Lines and Other Methods......12mo,   2 00
Stahl, A. W. Transmission of Power........................16mo,
Stahl, A. W., and Woods, A. T. Elementary Mechanism......12mo,   2 25
Standage, H. C. Leatherworkers' Manual....................8vo,   4 50
—— Sealing Waxes, Wafers, and Other Adhesives.............8vo,   *2 50
—— Agglutinants of All Kinds for All Purposes..............12mo,   3 50
Stanley, H. Practical Applied Physics...................(In Press.)
Stansbie, J. H. Iron and Steel..............................8vo,   2 50
Steadman, F. M. Unit Photography..........................12mo,   2 50
Stecher, G. E. Cork. Its Origin and Industrial Uses..........12mo,   1 00
Steinheil, A., and Voit, E. Applied Optics. Vols. I. and II. 8vo,
                                                        Each,   5 00
—— Two Volumes ....Set,   9 00
Steinman, D. B. Suspension Bridges and Cantilevers. (Science Series
    No. 127.) 0 75
—— Melan's Steel Arches and Suspension Bridges.............8vo,   *3 00
Stevens, A. B. Arithmetic of Pharmacy....................12mo,   1 50
Stevens, E. J. Field Telephones and Telegraphs.................   1 20
Stevens, H. P. Paper Mill Chemist.........................16mo,   4 00
Stevens, J. S. Theory of Measurements....................12mo,   *1 25
Stevenson, J. L. Blast-Furnace Calculations............12mo, leather,   2 50
Stewart, G. Modern Steam Traps...........................12mo,   *1 75
Stiles, A. Tables for Field Engineers.......................12mo,   1 00
Stodola, A. Steam Turbines.................................8vo,   7 50
Stone, E. W. Elements of Radiotelegraphy..........12mo, fabrikoid,   2 50
Stone, H. The Timbers of Commerce........................8vo,   4 00
Stopes, M. The Study of Plant Life.........................8vo,   2 00
Sudborough, J. J., and James, T. C. Practical Organic Chemistry.12mo,   3 50
Suffling, E. R. Treatise on the Art of Glass Painting........8vo,   *3 50
Sullivan, T. V., and Underwood, N. Testing and Valuation of Build-
    ing and Engineering Materials....................(In Press.)
Svenson, C. L. Handbook on Piping.........................8vo,   4 00
—— Essentials of Drafting..................................8vo,   1 75
—— Mechanical and Machine Drawing and Design.......(In Press.)
Swan, K. Patents, Designs and Trade Marks.................8vo,   2 00

Swinburne, J., Wordingham, C. H., and Martin, T. C.   Electric Currents.

Swoope, C. W.   Lessons in Practical Electricity 16mo,   0 75
.... 12mo,   2 50
Tailfer, L.   Bleaching Linen and Cotton Yarn and Fabrics 8vo,   7 00
Tate, J. S.   Surcharged and Different Forms of Retaining-walls .. 16mo,   0 75
Taylor, F. N.   Small Water Supplies 12mo,   3 00
—— Masonry in Civil Engineering 8vo,   *2 50
Taylor H. S.   Fuel Production and Utilization 8vo,   3 50
Taylor, W. T.   Calculation of Electrical Conductors 4to,   2 00
—— Electric Power Conductors and Cables .... 8vo (In Press.)
—— Calculation of Electric Conductors .... 4to (In Press.)
Templeton, W.   Practical Mechanic's Workshop Companion.
                                             12mo, morocco,   2 00
Tenney, E. H.   Test Methods for Steam Power Plants 12mo,   3 00
Terry, H. L.   India Rubber and its Manufacture 8vo,   3 00
Thayer, H. R.   Structural Design. 8vo.
    Vol.   I.   Elements of Structural Design 3 50
    Vol. II.   Design of Simple Structures 4 50
    Vol. III.   Design of Advanced Structures .... (In Preparation.)
—— Foundations and Masonry .... (In Preparation.)
Thiess, J. B., and Joy, G. A.   Toll Telephone Practice 8vo,   *3 50
Thom, C., and Jones, W. H.   Telegraphic Connections .... oblong, 12mo,   1 50
Thomas, C. W.   Paper-makers' Handbook .... (In Press.)
Thomas, J. B.   Strength of Ships 8vo,   2 50
—— The Powering of Ships 8vo,   10 00
Thomas, Robt. G.   Applied Calculus 12mo,   3 00
Thompson, A. B.   Oil Fields of Russia 4to,   10 00
—— Oil Field Development 15 00
Thompson, S. P.   Dynamo Electric Machines 16mo,   0 75
Thompson, W. P.   Handbook of Patent Law of All Countries 16mo,   2 00
Thomson, G.   Modern Sanitary Engineering 12mo,   *3 00
Thomson, G. S.   Milk and Cream Testing 12mo,   *2 25
—— Modern Sanitary Engineering, House Drainage, etc 8vo,   *3 00
Thomessen, E. G.   Soap-Making Industry .... 12mo (In Press.)
Thornley, T.   Cotton Combing Machines 8vo,   *3 50
—— Cotton Waste 8vo,   6 00
—— Cotton Spinning. 8vo.
—— Elementary Cotton Spinning 8vo,   5 00
    Second Year *3 50
    Third Year *2 50
Thurso, J. W.   Modern Turbine Practice 8vo,   *4 00
Thurston, A.   Pharmaceutical and Food Analysis .... (In Press.)
Tidy, C. Meymott.   Treatment of Sewage 16mo,   0 75
Tilmans, J.   Water Purification and Sewage Disposal 8vo,   2 50
Tinkler, C. K., and Masters, H.   Applied Chemistry 8vo,   4 50
Tinney, W. H.   Gold-mining Machinery 8vo,   *3 00
Titherley, A. W.   Laboratory Course of Organic Chemistry 8vo,   2 50
Tizard, H. T.   Indicators .... (In Press.)
Toch, M.   Chemistry and Technology of Paints 8vo,   4 50
—— Materials for Permanent Painting 12mo,   2 50
Tod, J., and McGibbon, W. C.   Marine Engineers' Board of Trade
    Examinations 8vo,   *2 00
Todd, J., and Whall. W. B.   Practical Seamanship 8vo,   9 00
Townsend, F.   Alternating Current Engineering .... 8vo, boards,   *0 75

Townsend, J. S. Ionization of Gases by Collision..............8vo,   *1 25
Transactions of the American Institute of Chemical Engineers, 8vo.
    Vol. XII., 1919. Two Parts................................Each,   5 00
    Vol. XIII. Part I, 1920...   5 00
    Vol. I. to XI., 1908-1918.........................8vo, each,   6 00
Traverse Tables 16mo,   0 75
Treiber, E. Foundry Machinery.................................12mo,   2 00
Trinks, W. Governors and Governing of Prime Movers...........8vo,   3 50
Trinks, W., and Housum, C. Shaft Governors................16mo,   0 75
Trivelli, A. P. H., and Sheppard, S. E. Silver Bromide Grain of
    Photographic Emulsions 8vo,   2 50
Trowbridge, W. P. Turbine Wheels..........................16mo,   0 75
Tucker, J. H. A Manual of Sugar Analysis....................8vo,   3 50
Turnbull, Jr., J., and Robinson, S. W. A Treatise on the Compound
    Steam-engine 16mo,   0 75
Turner, H. Worsted Spinners' Handbook......................12mo,   *3 00
Turrill, S. M. Elementary Course in Perspective..............12mo,   *1 25
Twyford, H. B. Purchasing.....................................8vo,   4 00
—— Storing, Its Economic Aspects and Proper Methods..........8vo,   3 50
Underhill, C. R. Solenoids, Electromagnets and Electromagnetic Wind-
    ings 12mo,   3 00
Underwood, N., and Sullivan, T. V. Chemistry and Technology of
    Printing Inks 8vo,   4 00
Urquhart, J. W. Electro-plating..............................12mo,   3 00
—— Electrotyping...12mo,   2 00
Usborne, P. O. G. Design of Simple Steel Bridges.............8vo,   *4 00

Van Nostrand's Chemical Annual. Fourth issue 1918.fabrikoid, 12mo,   *3 00
Van Wagenen, T. F. Manual of Hydraulic Mining.............16mo,   1 00
Vega, Baron Von. Logarithmic Tables.........................8vo,   2 50
Vincent, C. Ammonia and its Compounds. Trans. by M. J. Salter.8vo,   *2 50
Virgin, R. Z. Coal Mine Management..................(In Press.)
Volk, C. Haulage and Winding Appliances.....................8vo,   *4 00
Von Georgievics, G. Chemical Technology of Textile Fibres.....8vo,   7 00
—— A Text Book of Dye Chemistry........................8vo,   12 00
Vose, G. L. Graphic Method for Solving Certain Questions in Arithmetic
    and Algebra 16mo,   0 75
Vosmaer, A. Ozone...8vo,   *2 50

Wabner, R. Ventilation in Mines.............................8vo,   5 00
Wadmore, T. M. Elementary Chemical Theory...............12mo,   *1 50
Wagner, E. Preserving Fruits, Vegetables, and Meat........12mo,   *2 50
Wagner, H. E., and Edwards, H. W. Railway Engineering Estimates.
    (In Press.)
Wagner, J. B. Seasoning of Wood.............................8vo,   4 00
Waldram, P. J. Principles of Structural Mechanics..........12mo,   4 00
Walker, F. Dynamo Building.................................16mo,   0 75
Walker, J. Organic Chemistry for Students of Medicine........8vo,   4 00
Walker, S. F. Refrigeration, Heating and Ventilation on Shipboard
    fabrikoid, 12mo,   2 50
—— Electricity in Mining.......................................8vo,   *4 50
—— Electric Wiring and Fitting...............................8vo,   2 50

Wallis-Tayler, A. J. Bearings and Lubrication......8vo (*Reprinting.*)
—— Aerial or Wire Ropeways.................................8vo,   5 00
—— Preservation of Wood.......................................8vo,   4 00
—— Refrigeration, Cold Storage and Ice Making...............8vo,   5 50
—— Sugar Machinery...12mo,   3 00
Walsh, J. J. Chemistry and Physics of Mining and Mine Ventilation,
                                                              12mo,   2 50
Wanklyn, J. A. Water Analysis...............................12mo,   2 00
Wansbrough, W. D. The A B C of the Differential Calculus....12mo, *2 50
—— Slide Valves...12mo, *2 00
Waring, Jr., G. E. Sanitary Conditions.......................16mo,   0 75
—— Sewerage and Land Drainage...............................   *6 00
—— Modern Methods of Sewage Disposal...;....................12mo,   2 00
—— How to Drain a House.....................................12mo,   1 25
Warnes, A. R. Coal Tar Distillation...........................8vo, *5 00
Warren, F. D. Handbook on Reinforced Concrete...............12mo, *2 50
Watkins, A. Photography....................................8vo,   4 00
Watkins, G. P. Electrical Rates.............................8vo,   3 00
Watson, E. P. Small Engines and Boilers....................12mo,   1 25
Watt, A. Electro-plating and Electro-refining of Metals.........8vo,   5 00
—— Electro-metallurgy.......................................12mo,   1 00
—— Paper-Making 8vo,   4 00
—— Leather Manufacture 8vo,   6 00
—— The Art of Soap Making....,.............................8vo,   4 00
—— Electro-Plating 12mo,   2 00
Webb, H. L. Guide to the Testing of Insulated Wires and Cables. 12mo,   1 00
Wegmann, Edward. Conveyance and Distribution of Water for
                  Water Supply..............................8vo,   5 00
Weisbach, J. A Manual of Theoretical Mechanics..............8vo, *6 00
Weisbach, J., and Herrmann, G. Mechanics of Air Machinery....8vo, *3 75
Wells, M. B. Steel Bridge Designing.........................8vo, *2 5c
Wells, Robt. Ornamental Confectionery.......................12mo,   3 00
Weston, E. B. Loss of Head Due to Friction of Water in Pipes..12mo,   2 00
Whipple, S. An Elementary and Practical Treatise on Bridge Building.
                                                              8vo,   3 00
White, C. H. Methods of Metallurgical Analysis...............12mo,   3 00
White, G. F. Qualitative Chemical Analysis..................12mo,   1 40
White, G. T. Toothed Gearing................................12mo, *2 00
White, H. J. Oil Tank Steamers.............................12mo,   3 00
Whitehead, S. E. Benzol......................................8vo,   5 00
Whitelaw, John. Surveying...................................8vo,   4 50
Whittaker, C. M. The Application of the Coal Tar Dyestuffs...8vo,   3 00
—— Testing of Dyestuffs in the Laboratory...................8vo,   4 50
Widmer, E. J. Military Balloons............................8vo,   3 00
Wilcox, R. M. Cantilever Bridges...........................16mo,   0 75
Wilda, H. Steam Turbines...................................12mo,   2 00
—— Cranes and Hoists.......................................12mo,   2 00
Wilkinson, H. D. Submarine Cable Laying and Repairing......8vo,
                                              (*Reprinting.*)
Williamson, J. Surveying....................................8vo, *3 00
Williamson, R. S. Practical Tables in Meteorology and Hypsometry,
                                              4to,   2 50